Focus on World History

The Twentieth Century

Kathy Sammis

User's Guide
to
Walch Reproducible Books

Purchasers of this book are granted the right to reproduce all pages where this symbol appears.

This permission is limited to a single teacher, for classroom use only.

Any questions regarding this policy or requests to purchase further reproduction rights should be addressed to:

Permissions Editor
J. Weston Walch, Publisher
321 Valley Street • P.O. Box 658
Portland, Maine 04104-0658

1   2   3   4   5   6   7   8   9   10

ISBN 0-8251-4371-3

Copyright © 2002
J. Weston Walch, Publisher
P.O. Box 658 • Portland, Maine 04104-0658
www.walch.com

Printed in the United States of America

CONTENTS

UNIT 3. THE WORLD BETWEEN WARS: 1920S AND 1930S

UNIT 4. WORLD WAR II

UNIT 5. POSTWAR TO MILLENNIUM

UNIT 6. THE MODERN GLOBAL WORLD

TO THE TEACHER

This book, the fifth volume in Walch's *Focus on World History* series, covers the most recent era of world history, the twentieth century, when technology overcame physical barriers to create truly global communication networks. By the end of the century, computers and mass media sent and received messages to and from billions of people around the world, around the clock. The world economy became extremely integrated. Research and knowledge networks reached around the globe. A global mass culture developed, heavily influenced by Western elements. Standards of living rose in many regions, and new economic powers emerged, especially in the Pacific Rim.

Yet the twentieth century experienced much conflict, among nations and among rival ethnic and religious groups. The world's two most destructive wars took place during this era, each spanning the globe. Revolutions changed societies and life from Mexico and Turkey to Russia and China. Communist, fascist, and military dictators ruled many nations for long periods of time. Colonies struggled successfully for independence but then faced many challenges of nation-building. The threat of nuclear war hovered over the world during the Cold War between the United States and the Soviet Union. That threat was replaced at the turn of the millennium by the growing menace of international terrorism.

The reproducible student activities in this book are designed to draw students into this era of world integration, challenge, conflict, and change. They are designed to help students develop a richer understanding of the many elements of this varied time. Many activities in the book draw on original source materials, a device that personalizes what may seem like distant events for students.

Organization

The student activity topics are divided into units guided by the National Standards for History. (See end of this section.) Each unit begins with several Student Background pages, which give the most relevant information on that unit's topic. A number of reproducible student activity pages follow. These activities foster decision making, comprehension, analytical, comparative, interpretive, research, mapping, role-playing, interactive, and interdisciplinary skills in your students.

Each unit includes some Extra Challenge activities to provide enrichment for more advanced or adventurous students. Maps are provided for use with some activities; you can make copies as needed for applicable activities.

Each unit is preceded by a Teacher's Guide, giving you an overview of the unit and its objectives, plus specific teaching information on each student activity.

Lower-level students may have some difficulty reading the original source documents, which contain some formal, higher-level words and syntax. It may be helpful to go over some or all of the original source selections in class to be sure that each student has a full comprehension of them.

At the back of this book, you will find a section titled Answers, Additional Activities, and Assessments. For each unit, we have provided answers for the student activities, a list of suggested additional activities (including possible Internet sites to investigate), and several assessment vehicles. You'll also find additional teaching suggestions for some activities. The Additional Resources section includes titles of classic and recent literature from this era that will enrich students' learning and be helpful to you, plus CD-ROM and video titles and Internet sites with many links to world history sources.

Finally, the Glossary is reproducible for students' use.

Key to National Standards for World History	
Unit 1	Era 8, Standards 1A, 1B, 5
Unit 2	Era 8, Standards 2A, 2B, 5
Unit 3	Era 8, Standards 2C, 3A, 3B, 3C, 3D, 3E, 5
Unit 4	Era 8, Standards 4A, 4B, 5
Unit 5	Era 9, Standards 1A, 1B, 1C, 3
Unit 6	Era 9, Standards 2A, 2B, 2C, 2D, 2E, 2F, 3

TO THE STUDENT

The decades of the twentieth century were filled with change, progress, and strife. The nations of the world fought two global wars and many smaller conflicts. Science and technology transformed communications and lifestyles. Peoples and economies became globally linked.

The early decades of the twentieth century introduced many new inventions. Devices such as the telephone and the automobile changed both everyday life and the business world. Radios, newspapers, highways, and railroads drew people together. The world became truly modern. As it did, some people called for social reform. Others spurred revolution.

Also during the early 1900s, the nations of Europe became intense rivals. The competition broke out into war in 1914. This global conflict, World War I, caused a huge amount of damage and millions of deaths. The peace terms angered many nations.

During the 1920s, people in Europe worked for peace and enjoyed good times. The Great Depression of the 1930s rocked the world's economies. Nationalist movements grew in the colonies of the Middle East, Africa, and Asia. China fell into civil war. Military leaders gained control of Japan. Dictators ruled the Soviet Union, Germany, and Italy.

During the 1930s, Germany, Italy, and Japan followed a policy of expansion. Germany's moves in Europe caused a second global war, World War II. It was history's most destructive war yet. To end the war in the Pacific, the United States unleashed a terrifying new weapon—the atomic bomb. The world's nuclear age had begun.

The second half of the twentieth century was dominated by the Cold War. The United States and the Soviet Union clashed repeatedly around the world. But they did not get into a shooting war against each other. Meanwhile, colonies in Asia, Africa, and the Middle East gained their independence. They struggled to establish modern societies and cope with ethnic and religious divisions. China established a communist state beginning in the 1940s. But the Soviet Union collapsed in the 1990s. As the Cold War ended, the menace of international terrorism emerged.

The activities you'll be doing for this course of study will help you better understand this era of global links, revolution, and change. You'll work with maps. You'll put yourself into the shoes of this era's people. You'll describe your days in the trenches of World War I, devise revolutionary and nationalist strategies, and explain your life as a Chinese peasant. You'll read what this era's people said about themselves and others. You'll learn about the technology they invented and used and the art they created. When you're done, you'll have a better grasp of this most recent century of human history.

Name _____   Date _____

The World

**(For use with Unit 1, Worksheet 4; Unit 2, Worksheet 4;
Unit 5, Worksheet 3; Unit 6, Worksheet 3)**

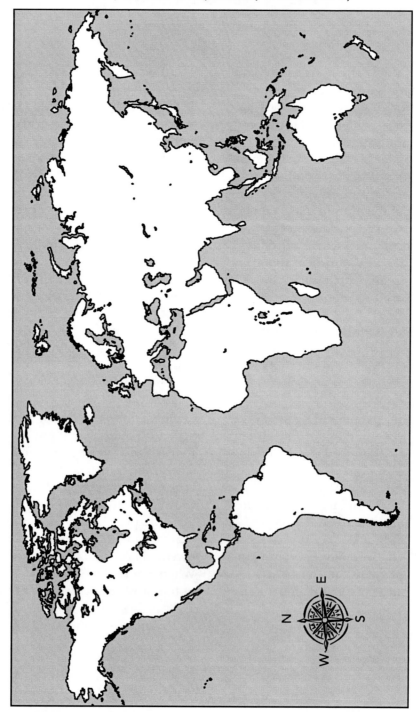

x   *Focus on World History: The Twentieth Century*

Name _____ Date _____

Europe

(For use with Unit 2, Worksheet 4)

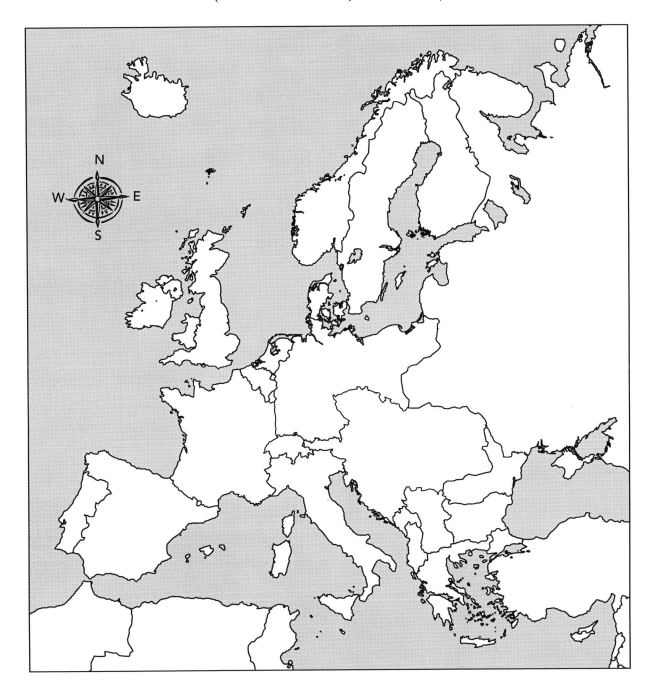

Latin America

(For use with Unit 3, Worksheet 16)

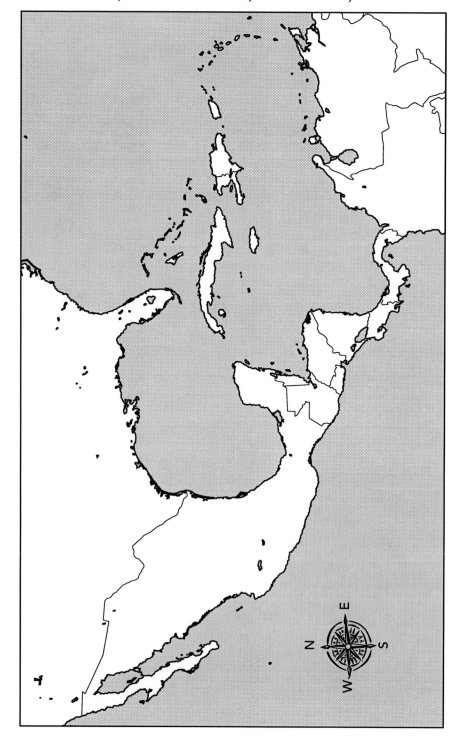

Name _____ Date _____

East and Southeast Asia

(For use with Unit 5, Worksheet 9)

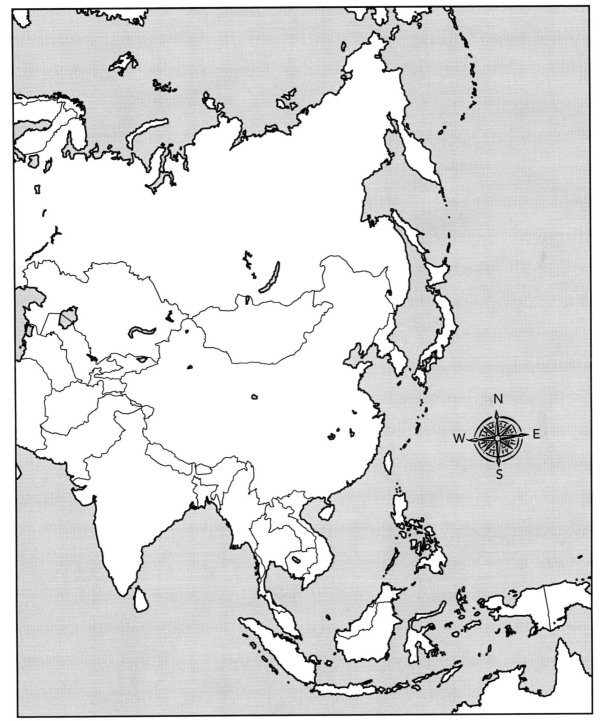

The Twentieth Century Begins

The objectives of this unit are to help students understand the conditions of the emerging world industrial economy and to help them examine the causes and consequences of emerging revolutionary movements in the early decades of the twentieth century. New technologies—such as the telephone, electric power, the assembly line and the automobile, and the airplane—changed both everyday life and business and industry. Modern communication and transportation systems linked people globally as never before in this new industrial world. Yet vast areas of the world remained rural, its people engaged in traditional, agriculturally based economies. Responses to the conditions of the modern industrial world ranged from status-quo conservatism to social reformism to socialism and communism and calls for revolution. The activities of this unit are designed to draw students into a better understanding of these early years of our most recently ended century.

Student Activities

Worksheet 1, New Technologies, presents six everyday technological innovations of the early twentieth century. Students supply details about each invention or development. The Extra Challenge invites students to describe the impact of each innovation on "their" life as a person of this time.

Worksheet 2, Industrial vs. Rural Life, provides a grid for students to fill in comparing specific elements of rural and industrial lives in the early 1900s.

Worksheet 3, Social and Political Ideas, presents statements of the time that express socialist, progressivist, and conservatist social/political ideologies; students label them appropriately. Students then choose one of the three ideologies to investigate further and finish with a role-play debate on which of the three is best suited to address conditions in a western country of their choice in the early twentieth century.

Worksheet 4, World Trade, World Environments, investigates the impact of world trade on world environments. Students trace global crop transfers, locate areas of raw material extraction, and describe adverse environmental effects of mining, railroad building, and cash-crop plantations. They finish by assessing a 1909 statement advocating the precedence of production for world trade purposes over production for self-sufficiency.

Worksheet 5, Urban Reforms, presents urban reformer Jacob Riis's description of dreadful living conditions in New York City's tenements near the turn of the century. Students identify the various hazards that Riis describes and tell how urban reforms in the early twentieth century improved these conditions.

Worksheet 6, The Mexican Revolution, provides a chart for students to fill in with details about the varied players in Mexico's turbulent, long-term revolution. The Extra Challenge invites students to assume the role of a Mexican peasant and explain his or her goals for the Revolution.

Worksheet 7, Revolutionary Art, presents a Diego Rivera mural panel, which students analyze for meaning and revolutionary message, both specific to the Mexican Revolution and universal to all revolutions.

Worksheet 8, Bloody Sunday, presents a graphic first-person account of the slaughter outside the tsar's Winter Palace in St. Petersburg in January 1905. Students describe the event, guided by a series of questions. The Extra Challenge invites students to develop a strategy, to write a pamphlet, or to create a poster that uses the events of Bloody Sunday to further the Russian revolutionaries' goals.

Worksheet 9, Life of Chinese Peasants, has students put themselves in the place of a Chinese peasant, describing various conditions of their life and explaining how Sun Yixian's "Three Principles of the People" might affect them. Students' answers reveal why the revolutionary movement appealed to China's vast peasant population.

The Twentieth Century Begins

As the twentieth century began, a new **industrial** world emerged. New **technologies** changed both everyday life and business and industry.

Inventions Change the World

Inventions of the late 1800s and early 1900s gave the world a new, more modern look. One big change was the use of electricity. The great American inventor Thomas Edison perfected the light bulb in 1879. He then developed ways to transmit electric power through a system of lines. An Edison system lit up New York City in 1882. Edison also developed the generator, which used electric power to run huge industrial machines. A factory could now be built anywhere, because it no longer needed water power. Cities became cleaner as electric trolleys replaced manure-producing horses.

> Thomas Edison also invented the phonograph (record player) and the motion picture (movies). Altogether, he patented more than a thousand inventions.

Thomas Edison

Inventions also changed communications radically. Alexander Graham Bell, a Scotsman who lived in the United States, patented the telephone in 1876. Networks of telephone lines soon spread across countries and around the world. By 1900, 1.5 million telephones were in use in the United States alone.

Alexander Graham Bell

> Bell demonstrated his amazing invention at the Philadelphia Exposition of 1876. The emperor of Brazil spoke into it. When a voice replied, the emperor exclaimed, "My word! It speaks!"

A young Italian inventor, Guglielmo Marconi, developed a way to send messages through the air, using radio waves instead of wires. He sent a wireless message across the Atlantic Ocean in 1901. After the vacuum tube was invented in 1904, radios could play music and human voices in people's homes.

(continued)

The Twentieth Century Begins *(continued)*

In the 1880s, inventors in Europe and the United States developed gasoline engines that powered a new vehicle—the automobile. But hand-built cars cost a lot to buy and to repair. American Henry Ford changed all that in the early 1900s. He designed a simple, reliable, affordable car called the Model T Ford. He cut production costs by creating the **assembly line.** A belt carried car frames past workers who each added a standard piece to the developing vehicle. Assembly line workers could create a Model T in a few hours. The price of a Model T dropped within the reach of most middle-class people. People from all over the world began buying them. The age of the automobile had begun.

Another huge change in transportation began in 1903. Americans Wilbur and Orville Wright made the first powered and sustained airplane flight that year. The airplane industry developed over the next few decades. Planes would play a part in World War I. In the 1920s, they began carrying mail and then passengers.

The New Industrial World

It was no accident that so much new technology developed in the early twentieth century. Starting in the late 1800s, companies began setting up research centers. They paid scientists and engineers to work in these labs, to develop and apply the best science and technology. The German chemical industry, backed by the German government, was a pioneer in this field. Edison set up one of the first research labs in the United States, and Bell's telephone company soon followed suit.

The people who lived and worked in this new industrial world were much more connected to the outside world than earlier people had been. News from around the world was rapidly reported in newspapers, on radio, and by telephone. Transportation systems also drew people together:

- Railroads crisscrossed Europe, Russia, and the Americas.
- As more and more people owned cars, highway networks spread across the land.
- Trucks hauled more produce and manufactured goods to more places.
- Steamships made the world's seas their highways.
- World trade increased. As factories produced more goods, manufacturers sought new markets around the globe. They also sought raw materials from nonindustrial lands.

(continued)

The Twentieth Century Begins (continued)

This modern industrial economy didn't grow at the same rate everywhere in the world. Great Britain, Germany, France, Japan, and the United States were very industrial. Southern, central, and eastern Europe were much less developed. Their economies remained mostly **rural,** based on agriculture. This was also true in much of Latin America, Africa, and Asia. Nations and **colonies** in these areas had little industry. The industrial nations looked to these less-developed areas to provide raw materials and to buy manufactured goods. Most of the people lived in rural areas and were poor farmers.

The lives of people in the industrial nations were quite different from those in rural nations. Western Europeans, for example, in general had more and better food, clothing, and shelter than their parents or grandparents had. They could usually change jobs if they wanted to. Women could find work outside the home. Rural **peasants** in countries like India, however, remained tied to the land. They had few choices about how they could lead their lives. They often did not have enough food, clothing, or shelter.

Reform and Revolution

Conditions in this newly modern, global world evoked varying responses:

- **Conservatives** favored the status quo (the way things were) and a society directed by market forces.
- Social reformers called for government action to correct social abuses and promote public welfare.

- **Socialists** called for public ownership of key industries, operated for the public welfare.
- **Marxists** predicted a class struggle between workers and employers. The workers would win, Marxists said. The workers would own all the means of production and share all the profits equally in a classless society.
- In some countries, radicals thought that conditions had become too much to bear. They called for revolution. They believed that only an overthrow of the existing political structure would allow the people's lives to get better.

Russia

Russia at the turn of the century remained an **autocracy.** The **tsar** ruled with an iron hand and blocked all calls for reform. The vast majority of people lived grueling lives of hard work and poverty, either on the land or in factories. Unrest spread, and revolutionary groups grew. The discontent came to a head in January 1905. A huge mass of workers and their families marched to the tsar's palace to ask for reforms. The tsar's soldiers shot hundreds of them. This "Bloody Sunday" event was a herald of the Russian Revolution that would erupt in the next decade.

Mexico

Mexico was under the harsh rule of dictator Porfirio Díaz from 1876 to 1911. During the early 1900s, more and more Mexicans called for reform and wanted Díaz out. Peasants wanted land, most of which was owned by a small, elite

(continued)

The Twentieth Century Begins *(continued)*

group. Workers wanted better wages and working conditions. Liberals wanted a republic with free elections.

Mexico's revolution began in 1910 and went on into the 1920s. It had a number of key leaders, each with his own followers. Sometimes they fought together, and at other times they fought each other. It was a period of disorder. But it finally produced the Mexican Constitution of 1917. This document brought the Mexican people many reforms, such as

- Land reform—large estates broken up, land given to peasants; government takes over Church lands
- Worker's rights—minimum wage, right to strike and join labor unions, equal pay for equal work
- Natural resources—would be owned by the government, not foreigners

China

In 1900, the foreign Manchus still ruled China as the Qing dynasty. In that year, the Boxer Rebellion broke out. It was a campaign against foreigners, who had forced the Qing rulers to grant them many special privileges. The Rebellion failed. But it made the Qing court realize they had to make some reforms to reduce foreign influence and improve their people's lives.

> Sun Yixian was a physician who spent many years in exile from China. He lived for a long time in the United States. He became famous when he escaped from agents of the Qing court who had kidnapped him in London.

Reforms moved slowly, however. The Qing court did not really embrace modern change or **nationalism.** Calls grew for a change in government. A principal voice was Sun Yixian (called Sun Yat-sen in earlier texts). His Revolutionary Alliance worked hard to bring down the Qing dynasty. Uprisings in 1911 accomplished the goal, and Sun became the first president of the new Chinese Republic. He soon realized he did not have the skills to run the nation. He gave his office to General Yuan Shikai, who quickly turned into a military **dictator.** When Yuan died in 1916, a disorderly period of rule by local warlords began. Revolution in China would continue for the next several decades.

New Technologies

Directions: Fill in the information about each innovation named below that became part of life in the early twentieth century.

1. Automobile
   Date(s) invented/developed:

   _____

   Person(s) who invented/developed:

   _____

   Country(ies) of origin:

   _____

2. Aircraft
   Date(s) invented/developed:

   _____

   Person(s) who invented/developed:

   _____

   Country(ies) of origin:

   _____

3. Electricity
   Date(s) invented/developed:

   _____

   Person(s) who invented/developed:

   _____

   Country(ies) of origin:

   _____

   Immediate environmental impact:

   _____

4. Telephone
   Date(s) invented/developed:

   _____

   Person(s) who invented/developed:

   _____

   Country(ies) of origin:

   _____

   Immediate environmental impact:

   _____

5. Typewriter (modern commercial version)
   Date(s) invented/developed:

   _____

   Person(s) who invented/developed:

   _____

   Country(ies) of origin:

   _____

6. Vacuum cleaner (electrically powered)
   Date(s) invented/developed:

   _____

   Person(s) who invented/developed:

   _____

   Country(ies) of origin:

   _____

Extra Challenge: Imagine you live in the early twentieth century. Describe how your everyday life is different because of each innovation named above.

Industrial vs. Rural Life

Directions: Compare rural to urban, industrial lives in the early 1900s by filling in the information on this chart. Respond by describing the most typical elements of life in each category.

Rural life	Feature	Industrial life
	Typical housing	
	Location within the country	
	Diet	
	Clothing	
	Employment	
	Health care	
	Leisure time and activities	
	Travel	
	Type of income	
	Education	
	Family structure	
	Life as a woman	

Social and Political Ideas

Part 1 Directions: A number of different social and political ideas competed in the early decades of the twentieth century. Among these were **socialism,** social reformism or **progressivism,** and **conservatism.** Label each statement below with the ideology it expresses.

> The history of mankind bears witness that the most necessary and fruitful reforms—the most durable measures—emanated from the supreme will of statesmen, or from a minority enlightened by lofty ideas and deep knowledge. On the contrary, the extension of the representative principle [right to vote] has ever been accompanied by a lowering of political ideas and opinions in the mass of the electors.
>
> Ideology: _____

> We call for the transformation of the capitalist private ownership of the means of production—land, mines, raw materials, tools, machinery, transport—into social ownership and the conversion of commodity production into socialist production, pursued by society for society's benefit.
>
> Ideology: _____

> Our party is committed to the principle of government by a self-controlled democracy expressing its will through representatives of the people. The supreme duty of the nation is the conservation of human resources through an enlightened measure of social and industrial justice.
>
> Ideology: _____

Part 2 Directions: To complete this activity, choose one of these ideologies to investigate further. Identify its main elements and the specific policies it promotes. Then select a western country of the early twentieth century, such as Germany or Russia, where these ideologies competed. With your classmates, role-play a debate among advocates of socialism, progressivism, and conservatism. Discuss which social/political system is best suited to address conditions in your nation at this time.

World Trade, World Environments

Part 1 Directions: Western desires for farm products and raw materials changed environments around the world in the early decades of the twentieth century. On your map of the world, a) trace the crop transfers noted below and b) locate and label the areas of raw material extraction noted.

Rubber trees, from Brazil to Malaya and Sumatra

Tea, from China to Ceylon, India, and Java

Cocoa, from South America to Africa

Cinchona tree (source of quinine) from Andes region to India, Java, and Ceylon

Oil-palm plantations, developed in Nigeria and Congo Basin

Gold mining, in South Africa, Australia, and Alaska

Tin mining, in Nigeria, Malaya, and Bolivia

Iron ore mining, in northern India

Copper mining, in Chile and central Africa

Part 2 Directions: Describe the adverse environmental effects of the following activities in the first decades of the twentieth century.

1. Mining _____

   _____

   _____

2. Railroad building _____

   _____

3. Cash-crop plantations _____

   _____

   _____

Part 3 Directions: Assess this 1909 statement by British botanist John Willis.

Whether planting in the tropics will always continue to be under European management is another question, but the northern powers will not permit that the rich and as yet comparatively undeveloped countries of the tropics should be entirely wasted by being devoted merely to the supply of the food and clothing wants of their own people, when they can also supply the wants of the colder zones in so many indispensable products.*

* from John Christopher Willis, *Agriculture in the Tropics: An Elementary Treatise.* Cambridge: Cambridge University Press, 1909

Urban Reforms

Living conditions for working-class people in industrial cities were dreadful at the beginning of the twentieth century. **Urban** reformers brought about many changes in the next few decades. Read this description of New York City **tenements** written by reformer Jacob Riis. It is from Riis's book *How the Other Half Lives*, published in 1890.

Take a look into this Roosevelt Street alley; just about one step wide, with a five-story house on one side that gets its light and air—God help us for pitiful mockery!—from this slit between brick walls. There are no windows in the wall on the other side; it is perfectly blank. . . .

Suppose we look into one [of the tenements]. . . . Be a little careful, please! . . . Here where the hall turns and dives into utter darkness is a step, and another, another. A flight of stairs. You can feel your way, if you cannot see it. . . . All the fresh air that ever enters these stairs comes from the hall door that is forever slamming, and from the windows of dark bedrooms that in turn receive from the stairs their sole supply of [air and light]. . . . That was a woman filling her pail by the hydrant you just bumped against. The sinks are in the hallway, that all the tenants may have access—and all be poisoned alike by their summer stenches. Hear the pump squeak! . . . In summer, when a thousand thirsty throats pant for a cooling drink in this block, [the pump] is worked in vain. . . . Listen! That short hacking cough, that tiny, helpless wail—what do they mean? . . . Oh! a sadly familiar story—before the day is at an end. The child is dying with measles. With half a chance it might have lived; but it had none. That dark bedroom killed it. . . .

Come over here. Step carefully over this baby—it is a baby, spite of its rags and dirt—under these iron bridges called fire escapes, but loaded down . . . with broken household goods, with washtubs and barrels, over which no man could climb from a fire. The gap between dingy brick walls is the yard. That strip of smoke-colored sky up there is the heaven of these people.*

* from Jacob Riis, *How the Other Half Lives*. New York: Charles Scribner's Sons, 1890

Directions: Identify the various hazardous conditions of the tenements that Riis describes. Then tell how urban reforms in the early decades of the twentieth century improved these conditions.

The Mexican Revolution

Directions: The Mexican Revolution went through a series of stages with many important players. Create a clear outline of the people and events involved by completing this chart.

	Family/ethnic background	Supporters	Years of rule or major activity	Fate
1. Porfirio Díaz				
2. Francisco Madero				
3. Victoriano Huerta				
4. Francisco "Pancho" Villa				
5. Emiliano Zapata				
6. Venustiano Carranza				
7. Alvaro Obregón				

Extra Challenge: As a Mexican peasant, explain your goals for the Revolution.

Revolutionary Art

Directions: Mexican artist Diego Rivera painted many murals depicting scenes of the Mexican Revolution. Shown here is a mural panel entitled "Formation of Revolutionary Leadership," also known as "Los Explotadores" ("The Exploited Ones"). Rivera created this artwork in 1926–27. It shows a mining inspector, an armed guard, a mine owner, and peasant mine workers. What are the meanings of the panel's titles? What aspects of the Mexican Revolution does Rivera express in this artwork? What universal themes of revolutionary movements does this artwork express?

Bloody Sunday

Directions: On January 22, 1905, thousands of workers marched to the tsar's Winter Palace in St. Petersburg, Russia. They carried holy icons (religious pictures) and pictures of the tsar. They had a petition for the tsar asking for help. A Russian Orthodox priest, Father George Gapon, led the march. Here is his description of what happened, from his 1905 book, *The Story of My Life*. Read it, and then answer the questions that follow.

> We started forward, singing in one mighty, solemn voice the Tsar's hymn, "God Save Thy People.". . . At the start the police not only did not interfere with the procession, but moved with us with bared heads in recognition of the religious emblems. . . . At last we reached within two hundred paces of where the troops stood. Files of infantry barred the road, and in front of them a company of cavalry was drawn up, with their swords shining in the sun.
>
> Suddenly the company of Cossacks galloped rapidly towards us with drawn swords. . . . Our front ranks broke before them, opening to right and left, and down this lane the soldiers drove their horses, striking on both sides. I saw the swords lifting and falling, the men, women, and children dropping to the earth like logs of wood, while moans, curses, and shouts filled the air. . . .
>
> Again we started forward, with solemn resolution and rising rage in our hearts. The Cossacks turned their horses and began to cut their way through the crowd from the rear. They passed through the whole column and galloped back. . . .
>
> We were not more than thirty yards from the soldiers . . . when suddenly, without any warning and without a moment's delay, was heard the dry crack of many rifle-shots. . . . I turned rapidly to the crowd and shouted to them to lie down. . . . As we lay thus another volley was fired, and another, and yet another, till it seemed as though the shooting was continuous. . . . An old man named Lavrentiev, who was carrying the Tsar's portrait, had been one of the first victims. . . . All the icons now lay scattered on the snow. . . .
>
> Horror crept into my heart. The thought flashed through my mind, "And this is the work of our Little Father, the Tsar.". . . Now I knew in very truth that a new chapter was opened in the book of the history of our people.

1. Imagine you are a Russian worker in 1905. Why would you have joined this march?
2. What were the workers asking the tsar in their petition?
3. Besides workers, what other people might have joined this march, and why?
4. Who ordered the soldiers to fire, and why?
5. What was the result of "Bloody Sunday"?

> **Extra Challenge:** As a member of a radical Russian group, discuss with comrades ways of using the events of Bloody Sunday to further the revolutionary cause. Or write a pamphlet or create a poster that uses the events to inflame public opinion and gain more supporters for your cause.

Life of Chinese Peasants

Part 1 Directions: Imagine you are a Chinese peasant, a farm worker, in the early 1900s. Explain the conditions of your life in the following areas.

1. Amount of land available for each person to farm:

2. Amount of harvest you can keep:

3. Your diet:

4. Threats of natural disaster:

5. Threat of crime:

6. Your special problem as a female:

7. Extra problems during the warlord period of 1915 into the 1920s:

Part 2 Directions: Explain how these "Three Principles of the People" promoted by Sun Yixian might affect you, the Chinese peasant.

1. Nationalism:

2. People's rights:

3. People's livelihood:

World War I

The objective of this unit is to help students understand the causes, course and nature, outcome, and consequences of World War I. While many Western people thought that war in Europe was a thing of the past, in fact powerful forces were at work through the early 1900s that drew the nations of Europe into their bloodiest, most destructive conflict yet. Chief among these forces were the intertwined elements of nationalism, imperialism, militarism, and an alliance system that guaranteed to draw in most of Europe in the event of conflict between any two members of opposing groups. The war, which in hindsight seems almost inevitable given the conditions of the times, erupted in August 1914. It was a new type of war, far more destructive than any previously, thanks to new weapons and appallingly high civilian casualties. While the war was fought largely in Europe, it also involved conflict in Asia, the Mideast, and Africa. The killing continued until 1917, when the United States finally entered the war and gave the Allies a winning boost. The victorious Allies dictated the peace terms, which treated Germany harshly and created great dissatisfaction among other combatants, both victors and losers. The peace agreements, in fact, sowed the first seeds of the next world war. The activities of this unit are designed to draw students into a better understanding of this first great global conflict of the twentieth century.

Student Activities

Worksheet 1, Causes of the War, presents a web diagram that students complete with information about the forces of nationalism, militarism, imperialism, and the alliance system that drew the nations of Europe into war.

Worksheet 2, Steps to War, presents the series of events from the June 28 assassination in Sarajevo to the British declaration of war on August 4. Students suggest alternative responses to each step that might have averted or slowed the progression to war. The Extra Challenge invites students to role-play a discussion among leaders of various Western nations about their responses to one or more of the named events.

Worksheet 3, The Tools of War, presents five new weapons of the war—machine gun, submarine (U-boat), tank, airplane (newly used as a combat weapon), and poison gas—with students describing each weapon and its destructive effect.

Worksheet 4, Mapping World War I, uses four different mapping exercises to increase students' familiarity with aspects of World War I, from conflicts earlier in the 1900s, to the war in Europe and around the world, to territorial changes in Europe as a result of the war.

Worksheet 5, Life and Death on the Western Front, presents vivid first-person accounts of life in the trenches and the adjoining no-man's land during the war. Students put themselves in the place of a trench-fighting World War I soldier and write a series of diary entries or letters home describing their experiences. The Answer section suggests some resources for students to read more about World War I soldiers' accounts as background for this activity.

Worksheet 6, The Appeal of War, presents verses from two patriotic World War I songs, "Over There" and "You'll Be There." Students identify expressions of patriotism, idealism, and excitement in the lyrics.

Worksheet 7, The Horror of War, presents verses from two poems written by World War I poet-soldiers that describe the grim reality of the war experience, a stark contrast to the songs of Worksheet 6. Students compare the visions of war expressed in the poems with the vision in the songs.

Worksheet 8, War Propaganda, presents two posters—a widely used propaganda tool—from World War I that promoted war aims, one Italian and one American. Students identify the war aim promoted and the emotional appeal, symbols, and slogans used in each poster to deliver the message. The Challenge Question asks students to speculate on why the graphic style of the two posters is so similar. The second page of the worksheet quotes slogans from actual World War I posters from a variety of nations and asks students to create new posters for one or more of the slogans.

Worksheet 9, War Casualties—World War I, presents country-by-country figures on military and civilian deaths in the war. Students analyze the figures by answering a series of questions and then use the figures in the chart to create a bar graph or pie chart of war casualties. The Extra Challenge invites students to compare prewar and postwar population figures in selected countries, calculating percentage differences.

Worksheet 10, Objections to the Peace Treaties, has students identify the objections of various nations, people, and regions to the provisions of the peace treaties signed at the end of World War I. This discontent would pave the way toward World War II.

World War I

In 1914, the countries of Europe had been at peace for many years. Some people thought that war on this continent was a thing of the past. But powerful forces had been at work through the early 1900s that would soon erupt into a devastating global war.

Causes of the War

One of the chief forces that pushed the nations of Europe toward war was nationalism. People's feelings of deep pride in their countries were very strong in Europe at this time. The countries of Europe became intense rivals:

- France, Great Britain, and Germany each followed a foreign policy of **imperialism.** They vied for control of colonies overseas.

- Germany and Great Britain sought to outdo each other in industrial output and military strength.

- France wanted revenge on Germany for its losses in the Franco-Prussian War of 1870–71.

- Austria-Hungary and Russia vied for influence in the Balkans. National feelings were strong among the many different ethnic groups of this region.

> "The Balkans" refers to the region of the Balkan peninsula, in southeastern Europe. Rivalries among its many different ethnic groups made the Balkans the "powder keg of Europe" in 1914—ready to explode at any minute.

The natural result of all this rivalry among nations was a buildup of military forces. Rival countries wanted to be sure their armies and navies were as strong as those of other nations. **Militarism**—glorifying the military and focusing on being ready for war—became a strong force. This was especially true in Germany, where military officers controlled government policy.

> A British cartoon of this time lampooned the arms race. A man declares, "We must build a bigger navy than the enemy will build when he hears we're building a bigger navy than he's building."

Next, distrust of rivals and fear of war led the great powers of Europe into **alliances.** (An alliance is an agreement among two or more nations that each will come to the aid of one of the others if it is attacked by any other country.)

- Germany, the empire of Austria-Hungary, and Italy formed the Triple Alliance.

- France, Russia, and Great Britain formed the Triple **Entente.** (An entente is a friendly understanding.)

Rather than ease tensions, these competing alliance systems raised them. Conflict between any two members of opposing groups could draw in all the other members. That is exactly what happened.

The War Begins

World War I began with an **assassination,** in the volatile Balkans. In 1908, Austria-Hungary had annexed Bosnia and Herzegovina, home to many Slavs. This outraged the neighboring Slavic state of Serbia.

(continued)

World War I *(continued)*

On June 28, 1914, the heir to the throne of Austria-Hungary made a state visit to Sarajevo, the capital of Bosnia. A teenage Serbian terrorist shot Archduke Franz Ferdinand and his wife Sophie dead in their open car.

> Serbian nationalists were furious that the archduke came to Sarajevo on June 28. This was the date when the Ottoman Empire conquered Serbia in 1389 and when Serbia regained its freedom in 1912. It was also the 14th wedding anniversary of Franz Ferdinand and Sophie.

The "powder keg" now rapidly exploded. Austria-Hungary blamed the Serbian government for the killings. So it declared war on Serbia on July 28. This brought the alliance system into play.

Russia supported Serbia, a fellow Slavic nation. It ordered the **mobilization** of its army. Germany responded by declaring war on Russia on August 1. France supported Russia, so Germany declared war on France also. To attack France, German troops swept through Belgium, a **neutral** nation. In response, an outraged Britain declared war on Germany.

The world war had begun. The fighting nations were aligned like this:

- France, Russia, Great Britain, and Italy were the Allied Powers. (Italy had left the Triple Alliance earlier.)

- Germany, Austria-Hungary, the Ottoman Empire (Turkey), and Bulgaria were the Central Powers.

A New Kind of War

World War I was unlike any war that had been fought before. It used new, highly destructive weapons. It involved civilians for the first time in a big way.

> The new weapons of World War I included the machine gun, the tank, the airplane, the submarine, and poison gas.

Armies were made up mostly of civilian recruits, not professional soldiers. Civilians at home were very involved. They worked in wartime industry, endured shortages of goods and food, and often found themselves in the middle of the bombing and artillery fire. They were also bombarded with government-sponsored war **propaganda** aimed at pumping up popular support for the war effort.

As the war began, both sides expected a quick win. Instead, the war raged all around the world from 1914 to 1918. It involved so many nations and people that it was known in its time as the Great War. Most of the battles were fought in Europe, but Africa and the Middle East saw fighting as well. Navies fought in seas everywhere.

(continued)

World War I *(continued)*

The Western Front

Germany had hoped for a swift victory by attacking France. But Allied forces stopped the Germans at the Battle of the Marne, near Paris. The war in the west then became a stalemate. Germany and France dug long lines of trenches along their shared border, the western front. Troops settled into the trenches. From time to time, groups of soldiers went "over the top" and tried to reach enemy trenches. No one made much progress, but thousands died trying.

> During the Battle of the Marne, the French forces desperately needed reinforcements. More than 600 taxicabs sped soldiers from Paris to the front.

The Eastern Front

The eastern front was along the border between Russia and the Central Powers—Germany and Austria-Hungary. War here shifted from hard-fought battles to periods of winter stalemate. The Russians suffered many defeats, but they kept Central Powers troops tied up and away from the western front. Great Britain and France, meanwhile, tried to gain access to the Black Sea via Gallipoli, in Turkey. This campaign failed, with a cost of many Allied dead and wounded.

> The Russian army was very poorly equipped. Some Russian soldiers sent into combat didn't even have rifles.

The War in Asia, the Mideast, and Africa

In the Mideast, Arabs helped British forces fight the Turks and end Ottoman rule. In Africa, the Allies took three of Germany's four colonies. In Asia, Japan (an ally of Britain) took German bases in the Pacific Ocean and China. Natives of British and French colonies fought in Europe.

The United States Enters the War

When World War I began, the United States had declared itself neutral. Most Americans wanted nothing to do with war in Europe. But the war on the seas drew the United States in. German submarines attacked and sank merchant and passenger ships sailing near Britain. Bowing to U.S. protests, Germany stopped these attacks in 1915.

By early 1917, Germany was struggling with severe food shortages at home, due in part to a naval blockade. German leaders decided once again to attack ships bringing supplies to Britain. They hoped to starve Britain into defeat before the United States responded to the ship sinkings by entering the war. The strategy failed. Americans were outraged at attacks on U.S. ships, and at a German plan to draw Mexico into the war. The U.S. Congress declared war on Germany in April 1917.

(continued)

World War I *(continued)*

The War Ends

Events in Russia in 1917 helped the Central Powers. Shortages of food and fuel, military failures, and corruption drove the Russian people to revolution. They swept away the tsar and set up a republic. The new Bolshevik rulers withdrew from the war. Germany could now concentrate almost all its forces on the western front.

The German army launched a last great offensive in France in the spring and summer of 1918. It almost succeeded, but fresh American troops gave the weary Allies a crucial boost. They pushed the Germans back, and the German ruler—the **kaiser**—had to step down. The new republic of Germany signed an **armistice** on November 11, 1918. The war was over.

World War I was incredibly expensive. More than 8 million people died in battle, and many more were wounded. Almost as many civilians died, from fighting, famine, and disease. Property losses were enormous. European nations were left unsettled, societies were unstable, and a lasting peace was elusive.

> The war killed millions of soldiers and civilians. But a worldwide epidemic of influenza—flu—killed even more. More than 20 million people around the globe died of this disease in 1918.

Searching for Peace

The fighting ended after Germany signed the armistice. For a lasting end to the war, the nations who took part had to work out and sign peace **treaties.** A conference to achieve this was held in 1919 in Paris, France.

Many nations took part in the peace conference. But the Big Three—Great Britain, France, and the United States—worked out the peace terms. These three nations had different agendas. U.S. President Wilson wanted a fair treaty that would achieve a lasting peace. Britain and France wanted to punish Germany and keep its military weak. Other nations pressed their own demands for changed borders and new lands.

> President Wilson called his terms for peace the Fourteen Points. They included an end to secret treaties, free trade, freedom of the seas, fair treatment of colonial people, arms reductions, and an association of nations to keep peace.

(continued)

World War I *(continued)*

After many heated arguments, the Big Three finally drew up the Treaty of Versailles. It treated Germany harshly:

- Germany had to accept full blame for causing the war.
- Thus, Germany had to pay **reparations**—payment for all civilian damage, a huge sum.
- Germany lost large chunks of its land to other nations, plus all of its overseas colonies.
- Germany had to shrink its military forces to a fraction of what they had been.

The Germans had no say in the terms of the treaty. They signed it because they had no other choice. But the German people were deeply angry about the treaty. They were bitter about being forced to admit "war guilt," and they felt that the high payments were unfair. These festering grievances helped pave the way to the next world war, as President Wilson warned would happen.

The other members of the Central Powers signed separate peace treaties. These and the Versailles Treaty changed the map of Europe. New nations were formed from lands that had been part of Germany, Austria, and Russia. The Ottoman Empire lost almost all its lands.

> The Versailles Treaty also created a League of Nations, an organization of the world's countries. The League was a cherished goal of Woodrow Wilson. But the U.S. Senate refused to allow the United States to join the League.

The peace treaties created many problems:

- Germans were bitter.
- Russia, which had been excluded from the peace talks, resented its land losses.
- People in Southwest Asia were angry that Ottoman rule was replaced by British and French control rather than independence.
- Diverse ethnic groups thrown together by the new borders in Europe were not pleased.
- Colonial people who had fought in the war were angry that their nations remained colonies.

This discontent did not bode well for continued peace in the coming decades.

Causes of the War

Directions: Powerful forces pushed the nations of Europe toward war in the early 1900s. Fill in the information to complete this web diagram about those forces.

1. **Nationalism**

   Definition: _____

   _____

   How it worked toward war:

   _____

   _____

   Specific examples: _____

   _____

   _____

3. **Imperialism**

   Definition: _____

   _____

   How it worked toward war:

   _____

   _____

   Specific examples: _____

   _____

   _____

Outbreak of war

2. **Militarism**

   Definition: _____

   _____

   How it worked toward war:

   _____

   _____

   Specific examples: _____

   _____

   _____

4. **Alliance system**

   Definition: _____

   _____

   How it worked toward war:

   _____

   _____

   Specific examples: _____

   _____

   _____

Extra Challenge: Debate with classmates the proposition that war in Europe was inevitable considering the nationalism, militarism, and imperialism of the times.

Steps to War

Directions: A series of events from June 28, 1914, to August 4, 1914, moved the nations of Europe to war, one step at a time. Those steps are described below. For each, suggest alternatives that might have derailed or slowed that progression toward war.

June 28, 1914—Archduke Franz Ferdinand visits Sarajevo amid reports of anti-Austrian unrest.

July 23, 1914—Austria presents Serbia with an ultimatum, backed by Germany.

July 25, 1914—Serbia accepts most, but not all, Austrian demands.

July 28, 1914—Austria rejects Serbia's offer, declares war on Serbia.

July 28, 1914—Russian leaders order mobilization of troops and move them toward Austrian-German border. Tsar Nicholas tells Kaiser Wilhelm II that the moves are only a precaution.

August 1, 1914—Germany declares war on Russia.

August 1, 1914—Germany demands that France remain neutral, but France backs its ally, Russia.

August 3, 1914—Germany responds by declaring war on France.

August 3, 1914—German army invades Belgium on its way to France.

August 4, 1914—Great Britain, honoring a treaty guaranteeing Belgium's neutrality, declares war on Germany.

Extra Challenge: With classmates, role-play a discussion among top leaders and advisors in Austria-Hungary, Serbia, Russia, Germany, France, and/or Great Britain in response to one or more of these events. Or deliver a speech defending your country's position and actions.

The Tools of War

Directions: Advances in military technology made World War I far more destructive than earlier wars. Describe each new weapon and tell how it made the Great War so terribly brutal and destructive.

1. Machine gun

   Description: _____

   _____

   Effect: _____

   _____

   _____

2. Submarine (U-boat)

   Description: _____

   _____

   Effect: _____

   _____

   _____

3. Tank

   Description: _____

   _____

   Effect: _____

   _____

   _____

4. Airplane

   Description: _____

   _____

   Effect: _____

   _____

   _____

5. Poison gas

   Description: _____

   _____

   Effect: _____

   _____

   _____

Cradle of Aviation Museum, Garden City, NY

Mapping World War I

Directions: Increase your understanding of World War I by completing these mapping exercises. Locate and label the listed items on the maps indicated. Also label all major bodies of water.

Part 1: Conflicts of the 1900s prior to World War I. Use your map of the world.

Russo-Japanese War 1904–05	First Balkan War 1912–13
Italo-Turkish War 1911–12	Second Balkan War 1913

Part 2: World War I in Europe. Use your map of Europe. Shade the nations that were the Allies in one color, and the nations that were the Central Powers in a contrasting color. Also, outline the Balkans, the western front, the eastern front, and the farthest advance to the east and the west by the Central Powers.

Allies			**Central Powers**		
France	Great Britain	Serbia	Germany	Austria-Hungary	
Russia	Italy		Bulgaria	Ottoman Empire	
Neutral			**Other**		
Spain	Switzerland	Norway	Belgium	Montenegro	
Albania	Netherlands	Sweden	Portugal	Greece	
Denmark	Luxembourg		Ireland	Romania	
Battles			**Cities**		
Marne	Tannenberg	Verdun	Paris	Vienna	Sarajevo
Somme	Gallipoli	Jutland	Berlin	Moscow	Brest-Litovsk

Part 3: The world at war. Use your map of the world. Show these regions that were involved in the war, and note with labels on the map how each was involved.

Southwest Asia	Africa	Europe	United States
East Asia	India	Brazil	Australia, New Zealand

Part 4: Territorial changes in Europe as a result of the war. Use your map of Europe, and compare the result with the Part II map.

Lands lost by Russia **(shade all in same color)**		**Changed/new states from** **old Austro-Hungarian Empire**		**Lands lost by Germany**
Finland	Estonia	Austria	Czechoslovakia	Polish Corridor
Latvia	Lithuania	Hungary	Yugoslavia	Alsace-Lorraine
Poland	Bessarabia	Romania		

Life and Death on the Western Front

Infantry soldiers in World War I lived for long stretches in trenches. When they emerged to attack, "no-man's land" confronted them. This was a barren and desolate killing ground between the Allied and German trench lines. Here are three men's accounts of their experiences on this western front.

Guy Empey, World War I soldier, 1917

The dugout was muddy. The men slept in mud, washed in mud, ate mud, and dreamed mud. I had never before realized that so much discomfort and misery could be contained in those three little letters, M U D. The floor of the dugout was an inch deep in water. Outside it was raining cats and dogs and thin rivulets were trickling down the steps. From the airshaft above me came a drip, drip, drip. . . . The air was foul. . . . It was cold.*

* from Guy Empey, *Over the Top*. Albany: Knickerbocker Press, 1917

Sir Philip Gibbs, World War I journalist, 1920

The rats—those big, lean, hungry rats of the trenches, who invaded the dugouts and frisked over the bodies of sleeping men—the lice that lived on the bodies of our men, the water-logged trenches, the shell-fire which broke down the parapets and buried men in wet mud, wetter for their blood, the German snipers waiting for English heads, and then the mines—oh, a cheery little school of courage for the sons of gentlemen!*

* from Sir Philip Gibbs, *Now It Can Be Told*. Garden City, NY: Garden City Publishing Co., 1920

Wilfred Owen, poet and World War I officer, 1917

[He describes marching across no-man's land at night.] It was too dark, and the ground was not sloppy mud, but an octopus of sucking clay, 3, 4, and 5 feet deep, relieved only by craters full of water. Men have been known to drown in them. . . . No Man's Land . . . is pockmarked like a body of foulest disease, and its odour is the breath of cancer. . . . There is not a sign of life on the horizon, and a thousand signs of death. Not a blade of grass, not an insect; once or twice a day the shadow of a big hawk, scenting carrion.*

* from Wilfred Owen, "Memoir" in *The Poems of Wilfred Owen*. New York: The Viking Press, 1931

Directions: Imagine you are a World War I soldier fighting from the trenches, crossing no-man's land. Write a series of diary entries or letters home describing your experiences. Tell about specific incidents, discomforts, and dangers. Add some humor to what you write. Share these accounts with classmates.

The Appeal of War

When the war began, people in the countries involved were very excited and patriotic. They looked forward to quick victory after dashing deeds on the battlefront. These lyrics from two patriotic songs of the times express these sentiments.

"Over There" by George M. Cohan

Johnnie get your gun, get your gun,
    get your gun,
Johnnie show the Hun,
    you're a son of a gun.
Hoist the flag and let her fly,
Like true heroes do or die.
Pack your little kit, show grit,
    do your bit,
Soldiers to the ranks from the
    towns and the tanks,
Make your mother proud of you,
And to liberty be true.

© Leo. Feist (NY), 1917, renewed 1945

"You'll Be There"
    words by J. Keirn Brennan
    music by Ernest R. Ball

Now the time has come when we must
    go to war,
You'll be there! You'll be there!
You will go just like your Daddy did before,
They have dared, we're prepared!
For our race was never known to run,
When they come we'll meet them gun to gun,
North and South, yes, ev'ry mother's son,
You'll be there! You'll be there!

© M. Witmark & Sons, 1915

Directions: Identify the expressions of, and appeal to, patriotism, idealism, and excitement in these lyrics.

1. Patriotism: _____

   _____

2. Idealism: _____

   _____

3. Excitement: _____

   _____

Extra Challenge: Find sheet music for these two songs and—solo or with classmates—perform them for the class. You could perform, or play recordings of, other World War I songs as well.

The Horror of War

The reality of war soon erased the appeal of war for the soldiers on the front. Siegfried Sassoon and Wilfred Owen were English officers who were also poets. Many of their poems vividly expressed the dreadful reality of the war experience.

"Dulce et Decorum Est," final verse
    by Wilfred Owen
[A sudden gas attack fills one soldier's lungs.]
He plunges at me, guttering, choking, drowning.
If in some smothering dreams, you too could
    pace
Behind the wagon that we flung him in,
And watch the white eyes writhing in his face,
His hanging face, like a devil's sick of sin;
If you could hear, at every jolt, the blood
Come gargling from the froth-corrupted lungs,
Bitter as the cud
Of vile, incurable sores on innocent tongues,—
My friend, you would not tell with such high zest
To children ardent for some desperate glory,
The old Lie: Dulce et decorum est
Pro patria mori.*

* from Wilfred Owen, "Dulce et Decorum Est" in *Poems*. London: Chatto and Windus, 1920

"Suicide in the Trenches"
    by Siegfried Sassoon
I knew a simple soldier boy
Who grinned at life in empty joy.
Slept soundly through the lonesome dark,
And whistled early with the lark.

In winter trenches, cowed and glum,
With crumps and lice and lack of rum,
He put a bullet through his brain.
No one spoke of him again.

You smug-faced crowds with kindling eye
Who cheer when soldier lads march by,
Sneak home and pray you'll never know
The hell where youth and laughter go.*

* from Siegfried Sassoon, "Suicide in the Trenches" in *Counterattack*. New York: E. P. Dutton & Company, 1918

Directions: Compare these poems with Cohan's lyrics for "Over There" and Brennan's lyrics for "You'll Be There" (Worksheet 6). What elements of the poems contrast sharply with the song lyrics?

War Propaganda

Directions: Propaganda posters were an important part of World War I. All the major nations used them to promote various war aims. Study the posters shown on this page. Then answer these questions about each one: What war aim does this poster promote? (If you do not know Italian, try to figure out what the Italian poster might be promoting, based on the images.) What emotional appeal, symbol, or slogan does the poster use to get its message across?

1. War aim: _____

   Appeal, symbol: _____

   _____

   _____

   _____

2. War aim: _____

   Appeal, symbol, slogan: _____

   _____

   _____

   _____

Challenge Question: Why do you think the graphic style of these two posters, from two different countries, is so similar?

(continued)

War Propaganda (continued)

Directions: Quoted below are slogans from World War I posters from a variety of countries. Choose any that interest you, and create actual posters with images that seem to you to be appropriate to promote the aims of the slogan.

On Her Their Lives Depend—
Woman Munition Workers—
Enroll at Once
(Great Britain)

That Liberty Shall Not Perish
From the Earth—Buy Liberty
Bonds
(United States)

A Last Effort—And We Will
Go On
(France)

Who's Absent?—Is It You?
(Great Britain)

Following the Paths of Our
Fathers in the Ranks of the
Polish Army for Motherland
and Freedom
(Poland)

For the Flag! For Victory!
Subscribe to the National Loan
(France)

Beat Back the Hun with
Liberty Bonds
(United States)

For France—Deposit Your
Gold—Gold Fights for Victory
(France)

Farm to Win "Over There"—
Join the U.S. Boys' Working
Reserve—The Army Behind
the Army
(United States)

1805—England Expects—
1915—Are You Doing Your
Duty Today?
(Great Britain)

War Casualties—World War I

Directions: Given below are estimated numbers of military personnel and civilians who died in World War I, broken down by country. First, answer the questions about the figures. Then, use the figures to create a bar graph or pie chart of war casualties.

DEATHS IN WORLD WAR I		
Country	Military deaths	Civilian deaths
Germany	1,800,000	800,000
Russia	1,700,000	2,000,000
France	1,400,000	40,000
Austria-Hungary	1,000,000	300,000
British Empire	1,000,000	30,000
Italy	600,000	*
Romania	335,000	275,000
Ottoman Empire	325,000	2,150,000
Bulgaria	75,000	27,000
United States	50,000	*
Serbia	45,000	650,000
Belgium	15,000	30,000

* Figures are not available; losses in each case were quite small.

1. Which country had the greatest loss of life? _____

2. How many military deaths did the Central Powers suffer? _____

3. How many military deaths did the Allied countries included in the figures above suffer?

   _____

4. Which country had the greatest number of civilian deaths? _____

   What accounts for this? _____

5. Which countries had very few civilian deaths? _____

   What accounts for this? _____

   _____

Extra Challenge: Compare immediate prewar and postwar population figures in Germany, Russia, and France, and calculate the percentage difference for each country.

Objections to the Peace Treaties

Directions: The Allies wrote peace treaties that the Central Powers had to sign at the end of World War I. Rather than create a stable peace, the treaties aroused anger and discontent among people around the world. Explain what these nations, people, and regions objected to about the treaty provisions.

1. Germany: _____
   _____

2. Italy: _____
   _____

3. Japan: _____
   _____

4. Middle Eastern Arabs: _____
   _____

5. China: _____
   _____

6. Russia/Soviet Union: _____
   _____

7. India: _____
   _____

8. Africa: _____
   _____

The World Between Wars: 1920s and 1930s

The objective of this unit is to help students understand the varied events of the 1920s and 1930s, including the aftereffects of World War I, the Great Depression, the growth of nationalist movements in Asia and Africa, revolution in China and revolutionary change in Russia, the rise of dictators in Italy and Germany, and activities in the Americas. People in postwar Europe yearned for peace and felt anxious about the future, yet participated in a lively mass culture. Economies around the world were rocked by the global effects of the Great Depression. U.S. foreign policy was highly interventionist in regard to Latin America but firmly isolationist as to the rest of the world. Strong nationalist movements in European-controlled colonies in the Middle East, Egypt, and India pushed for independence. China's Nationalists and Communists moved into a civil war that Japanese invasion temporarily halted. Lenin and Stalin established a dictatorial communist state in the Soviet Union, while Mussolini and Hitler established dictatorial fascist states in Italy and Germany. The activities of this unit are designed to draw students into a better understanding of these eventful, challenging years between the two world wars.

Student Activities

Worksheet 1, Different Paths in Europe, has students identify the types of government and specific leaders in major countries of Europe during the between-wars years. The Challenge Questions ask students to discern a geographic-political pattern from the information they have recorded.

Worksheet 2, Words of the Times, presents statements made by various nationalist, independent, and revolutionary leaders of the 1920s and 1930s; students match listed leaders' names with statements.

Worksheet 3, Changes in the Middle East, is a mapping exercise that familiarizes students with changes in the Middle East following World War I, which created some of the modern Arab nations of today.

Worksheet 4, Nationalism in Southwest Asia and India, presents a web diagram that students fill in with key elements of nationalist movements in Turkey, Iran, Saudi Arabia, and India, demonstrating points of similarity and contrast. The Extra Challenge invites students to role-play discussions among people from these nations about how the nationalist movements have and have not changed their lives.

Worksheet 5, Nonviolence: Theory and Practice, contrasts Gandhi's expression of the tactic of nonviolent noncooperation with a vivid newspaper account of the Salt March beatings of passive protesters. Students explore the concept of nonviolent protest by answering questions about the readings. The Extra Challenge invites students to write a letter to Gandhi suggesting possible effective alternatives to nonviolent protest.

Worksheet 6, Revolution in China, has students put themselves into the place of a variety of different hypothetical Chinese people and describe which side each would support, the Kuomintang or the Communists, and why. Students follow up by explaining Mao Zedong's metaphorical description of the Long March retreat as a victory.

Worksheet 7, Marxism: Theory and Practice, presents Engel's and Marx's descriptions of Marxist communism; students explain the ways in which Lenin, Stalin, and Mao Zedong adapted classic Marxism to fit their particular situations and goals.

Worksheet 8, "The Crisis of the Spirit," presents French author Paul Valéry's expression of the widespread postwar doubt, despair, and anxiety. Students give examples of paintings, music, poetry, and novels that express the postwar anxieties.

Worksheet 9, Women's Lives, puts students in the place of hypothetical women in various nations around the world, explaining the ways in which life changes under the described circumstances of the times. The Extra Challenge invites students to partner with a classmate and become "pen pals" as two women from different countries as described on the worksheet.

Worksheet 10, Time Line of the Russian Revolution, presents events involved with the Russian Revolution, from beginnings in the early 1900s through the aftermath of the Bolshevik takeover in 1917. Students date the events, classify them under four phases of the Revolution, and then create a time line.

Worksheet 11, The Soviet Economy, presents a Venn diagram that students fill in to compare features of Lenin's New Economic Policy and Stalin's Five-Year Plans.

Worksheet 12, Communism, Fascism, Democracy, presents a chart that students fill in with details to create a succinct comparison of these three political systems.

Worksheet 13, Mass Culture, has students explain the elements of mass culture across national lines that are shown in three images from this era.

Worksheet 14, The Great Depression, uses graphics to help students better understand elements of the global economic crisis. Students identify elements of the triangular flow of cash among the United States, Germany, and France/Britain, and explain details of the downward industrial economic spiral. The Extra Challenge invites students to construct a similar spiral for the farm economy.

Worksheet 15, Scenes of the Great Depression, presents two images that express effects of the Great Depression in the United States; students use what they know about the Great Depression to write a narrative for each, telling the story behind the picture.

Worksheet 16, Latin America and the United States, uses mapping to familiarize students with the many nations of Latin America in which the United States intervened in the early decades of the twentieth century. On the worksheet, students identify information about each instance of intervention, as a key to accompany their map.

The World Between Wars: 1920s and 1930s

The Postwar World

World War I ended in 1918. People around the world in the 1920s yearned for peace. Peace groups held many large conferences. Nations signed a variety of peace agreements. But many nations and ethnic groups were unhappy with the Versailles Treaty and the new national boundaries it set up.

Political discontent was not the only problem that plagued people in the 1920s. World War I had been horribly destructive and brutal. The lives of the people of Europe had been shattered. So had these people's faith in unstoppable progress and the ability of the human spirit to solve all problems. Many postwar people felt anxious and unsure about the future. They feared the destructive uses that modern technology could be turned to. They had become well aware of the darker side of human nature.

At the same time, a lively mass culture and consumer economy developed in the western world. Mass-market magazines and newspapers brought timely news and information from around the world. Advertisements touted a wide array of exciting consumer goods. Most middle-class people could afford to buy these items. Families enjoyed radio shows at home and flocked to view films in nearby theaters. Sports became popular leisure-time activities.

The Great Depression

The 1920s were a time of peace and prosperity in the western world. The 1930s were quite different. A worldwide economic slump began in the United States in 1929. The slump soon became a **depression**—a period of low economic activity and high unemployment. This depression spread rapidly to Europe, and on to the rest of the world.

- Banks failed, and people lost their life savings.
- Millions of people could not find a job. They lined up at soup kitchens for meals.
- World trade slowed to a trickle.

Recovery was slow. The bad economic times spurred the rise of dictators across much of Europe. The democratic nations of Britain, France, and the United States used government programs to help revive their economies.

The Western Democracies

Great Britain

Great Britain had borrowed money, from its own people and the United States, to pay the costs of World War I. Now it had a huge war debt to pay off, so people had to pay high taxes. Britain's share of world trade had fallen during the war, and it did not fully recover in the postwar years. Government control shifted between the Conservative and Labour parties during the 1920s and 1930s. The middle and upper classes supported the Conservative party. Workers supported the Labour Party.

(continued)

The World Between Wars: 1920s and 1930s *(continued)*

France

France was devastated by World War I. Many of its young men had been killed. Buildings, land, roads, bridges, and railroads all needed rebuilding. Like Britain, France had huge war debts to pay off. France also had to keep up its military strength in case of future German attack. The French people couldn't agree on how to take care of these problems. They divided into many political parties and groups, which formed ever-changing **coalitions.**

The United States

The U.S. economy had benefited from the production of war supplies and food during the war. Most people enjoyed the mass culture and good times of the 1920s. But the Great Depression hit very hard in the United States during the 1930s. Little help was available at first. The reforms known as the **New Deal** helped the U.S. economy revive.

> The people elected Franklin D. Roosevelt as U.S. president in 1932. He quickly started a wide-ranging program of government-run social and economic reforms. The program was called the New Deal.

Most Americans had believed it was necessary to enter the war in 1917. But by 1919, many Americans were sick of the war and of Europe's problems. So during the 1920s, the United States pulled back into a policy of **isolationism.** It mostly kept itself apart from international affairs.

Latin America

One arena in which the United States definitely did not pursue a policy of isolation was Latin America. The Panama Canal was built between 1903 and 1914, when it opened. The canal linked the Pacific Ocean and the Caribbean Sea. The United States considered this new link vital for its military and trade interests.

> For many years, U.S. policy had been to prevent any European meddling in the affairs of countries in the Americas. This policy was known as the Monroe Doctrine.

To protect this link, U.S. President Theodore Roosevelt declared that the United States had a right to take "police action" in Latin America. The United States would act as a "police force" to correct any unstable situations in any Latin American nations. In practice, an "unstable" condition was anything that threatened U.S. business interests. The United States exercised control in many Latin American nations between 1905 and the 1930s. This caused many Latin Americans to resent the United States deeply.

> U.S. interference in Latin America to protect U.S. business was called "dollar diplomacy." It was replaced with Franklin Roosevelt's new "Good Neighbor" policy in the mid-1930s.

(continued)

The World Between Wars: 1920s and 1930s *(continued)*

The Middle East, Egypt, and India

People from European colonies fought in Allied armies during World War I. The Allies had said that one aim of the war was to protect the right of all people to self-government. After the war, former German and Ottoman colonies became **mandates** of the League of Nations. Each former colony was assigned to one of the Allies. The Allies had a mandate (requirement) to prepare these colonies for eventual freedom. These factors gave a large boost to nationalist feelings in many colonies.

The Middle East and Egypt

In the Middle East, both Jews and Arabs thought they had a right to Palestine after the war. Britain allowed oil-rich Iraq to become an independent kingdom in 1932.

Army officer Mustafa Kemal led a revolution in the remnant of the Ottoman Empire. He created the Republic of Turkey. His sweeping changes transformed Turkey from a traditional Islamic nation into a modern Western-style democracy.

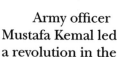

> Mustafa Kemal renamed himself Kemal Atatürk, which means "Father of the Turks."

Persians resented the **spheres of influence** in their nation controlled by Britain and Russia.

In 1925, army officer Reza Shah took over the throne. He renamed himself Reza Shah Pahlavi and his country Iran. Like Atatürk, he made Iran a modern nation along Western lines, ruling as a monarch.

Great Britain declared Egypt independent in 1922. But British troops remained in Egypt to protect British use of the Suez Canal. In 1936, Britain agreed that British forces would keep control of the Suez Canal for only another 20 years.

India

India was a British colony, and it had provided important support for Britain during the war. Educated Indians felt strongly that India deserved independence in return. But the nation was divided between the two main religious groups, Muslims and Hindus. They had deep differences. The Hindus themselves were deeply divided into separate classes called **castes.**

A Hindu nationalist leader, Mohandas Gandhi, inspired unified support. He developed a type of political protest that he called "nonviolent noncooperation." Today, we call this **passive resistance** or **civil disobedience.** Gandhi had his supporters refuse to cooperate with government policies and orders. Indian mass resistance, and very bad worldwide publicity about it, wore the British down. Bit by bit, they gave more and more self-rule to India.

> Gandhi inspired the Indian masses with his spiritual nature. The people called him Mahatma, "the saintly one."

(continued)

The World Between Wars: 1920s and 1930s *(continued)*

China

Mao Zedong helped found the Chinese Communist party in 1921. Mao's Communists promoted land reform and secured the support of peasants and urban workers. General Jiang Jieshi (called Chiang Kai-shek in earlier texts) became head of the Nationalist party, or Kuomintang, in 1925. Jiang's government became corrupt and did nothing to help the masses of Chinese peasants.

Mao Zedong

The Communists and Nationalists fought together against local warlords. But in 1927, Jiang turned on the Communists and had many of them killed. By 1930, the Kuomintang and Communists were fighting a civil war. It was put on hold when Japan invaded China in 1937.

> The Communists were badly outnumbered. They had to retreat on a 6,000-mile "Long March" to northern China from 1934 to 1935.

Japan

Japan had become both an industrial and an imperial power in the early 1900s. During the 1920s, the nation became more democratic. The parliament passed a few social reforms.

The Great Depression hit Japan hard in 1930, as it crippled world trade, the basis of Japan's economy. Military leaders gained control of the government, ruling in the name of the emperor. They restarted a policy of foreign expansion, to secure the markets and raw materials Japan needed. Their overseas moves were the first steps toward World War II.

The Soviet Union

After the Russian Revolution of 1917, V. I. Lenin led the new Communist government. It took ownership of all land and all industries in Russia. It also renamed Russia as the Union of Soviet Socialist Republics, or U.S.S.R. It was also called the Soviet Union. The central Soviet government in Russia strictly controlled the nation. The Communist party controlled the government, and Lenin controlled both of them.

> The **soviets** of the U.S.S.R. were the councils of workers and soldiers that had formed during the revolution. The republics were the separate regions of the nation.

Josef Stalin took control after Lenin's death in 1924. His Communist party ran the Soviet economy by Five-Year Plans. They set high quotas for products of industry and very low quotas for consumer goods. Peasants were forced at gunpoint to join huge industrial farms called **collectives.** Stalin also made the Soviet Union into a **police state.** Secret police, party spies, and **purges** kept Soviet citizens under strict control.

(continued)

The World Between Wars: 1920s and 1930s *(continued)*

Italy

After World War I, Italy struggled with high war debt, rising prices, and a lack of jobs. Violence flared, and the government was weak. A strong leader emerged—Benito Mussolini, head of the **Fascist** party. In 1922, Mussolini had himself named **premier,** with wide powers to restore order. Soon Mussolini made himself dictator.

Mussolini set up a **totalitarian** state, a system in which the state and its leader have nearly *total* control. People lost the right to vote, to speak and publish freely, to go on strike. The government controlled the economy. Like the U.S.S.R., Italy became a police state. It also became a strongly nationalist and militarist nation. Mussolini's moves to expand Italy's power and wealth beyond its borders were more steps toward World War II.

Benito Mussolini

Germany

Germany too was in chaos after World War I. Its people blamed their new civilian leaders for the war's poor outcome. Jobs were scarce. To pay high war debt and reparations, the German government printed more and more money. **Inflation** soared completely out of control.

As in Italy, a strong leader emerged out of the chaos. He was Adolf Hitler, head of the National Socialist German Workers' party, or the Nazi party for short. Hitler and his party blamed communists, liberals, and Jews for Germany's woes. His stirring speeches pledging to restore Germany to its former glory attracted widespread support.

Hitler accepting ovation at Reichstag

Hitler took control of Germany in 1933. He turned Germany into a police state. He also had laws passed that stripped Jews of most of their civil and property rights. He declared that Germany had a right to expand. Hitler's pursuit of this policy to expand, bit by bit, built more steps toward World War II.

Different Paths in Europe

Directions: The countries of Europe followed different political paths after World War I. Outline these paths by filling in the information below. Then answer the Challenge Questions that follow.

1. England
   Type of government:
   _____
   _____
   Leader(s):
   _____
   _____

2. France
   Type of government:
   _____
   _____
   Leader(s):
   _____
   _____

3. Italy
   Type of government:
   _____
   _____
   Leader(s):
   _____
   _____

4. Germany
   Type of government:
   _____
   _____
   Leader(s):
   _____
   _____

5. Poland
   Type of government:
   _____
   _____
   Leader(s):
   _____
   _____

6. Czechoslovakia
   Type of government:
   _____
   _____
   Leader(s):
   _____
   _____

7. Hungary
   Type of government:
   _____
   _____
   Leader(s):
   _____
   _____

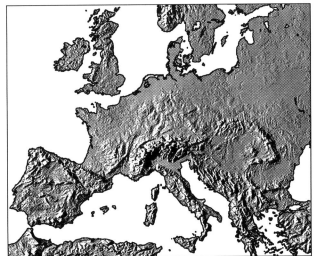

Challenge Questions:
   1. What geographic-political pattern do you see in post-World War I Europe?
   2. Why might this be?

Words of the Times

Directions: Many nationalist, independent, and revolutionary leaders played large roles on the world stage during the 1920s and 1930s. Match each statement below with the leader who uttered it.

_____ 1. "We are ready to fight on, and I cannot believe that the great rulers here assembled will treat us as did our former oppressors [the Ottoman Turks]."

_____ 2. "Nonviolent resistance is superior to the force of arms. One who is free from hatred requires no sword."

_____ 3. "The force of the peasantry is like that of the raging winds and driving rain. No force can stand in its way."

_____ 4. "The principal of autocracy will be maintained by me as firmly and unswervingly as by my lamented father."

_____ 5. "I will lead our nation back to her ways of ancient greatness. . . . Fascism conceives of the State as an absolute."

_____ 6. "Surviving in the world of modern civilization depends upon changing ourselves. . . . A civilized, international dress is worthy and appropriate for our new nation."

_____ 7. "Even though we have 400 million people gathered together in one China, in reality, they are just a heap of loose sand, for they do not have national spirit."

_____ 8. "The whole world is now passing into a movement which must give rise to a world socialist revolution."

_____ 9. "If others speak of the World and Humanity, we must say the Fatherland—and only the Fatherland!"

_____ 10. "We are 50 or a hundred years behind the advanced countries. We must make good this distance in 10 years."

a. Sun Yixian

b. Tsar Nicholas II

c. Emir Faisal

d. Adolf Hitler

e. Josef Stalin

f. Lenin

g. Benito Mussolini

h. Mohandas Gandhi

i. Kemal Atatürk

j. Mao Zedong

Josef Stalin

Changes in the Middle East

Directions: The Versailles Treaty changed the map of the Middle East after World War I. On this map of the Middle East and Egypt/Sudan, draw boundary lines for the League of Nations mandate areas. Shade the areas that were part of the Ottoman Empire when the war began. Label the following mandate areas and countries.

Mandate areas		
Syria	Transjordan	Lebanon
Iraq	Palestine	

Other

Egypt	Saudi Arabia	Turkey	Kuwait	Qatar
Bahrain	Trucial States	Yemen	Aden	Muscat and Oman
Anglo-Egyptian Sudan				

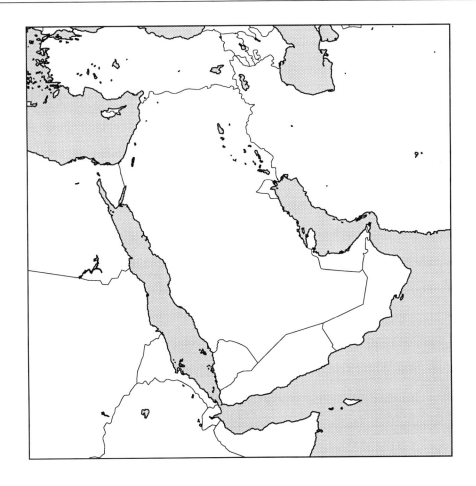

Nationalism in Southwest Asia and India

Directions: Strong nationalist movements developed in Southwest Asia and India after World War I. (The movement in Saudi Arabia began in the early 1900s.) Identify key elements of these movements by filling in this web diagram. When completed, the diagram will show the points of similarity and contrast among these nationalist movements.

1. **Turkey**

   Leader: _____
   _____

   Goals: _____
   _____
   _____

   Changes: _____
   _____
   _____

3. **Iran (Persia)**

   Leader: _____
   _____

   Goals: _____
   _____
   _____

   Changes: _____
   _____
   _____

Nationalist movements
1920s and 1930s

2. **Saudi Arabia**

   Leader: _____
   _____

   Goals: _____
   _____
   _____

   Changes: _____
   _____
   _____

4. **India**

   Leader: _____
   _____

   Goals: _____
   _____
   _____

   Changes: _____
   _____
   _____

Extra Challenge: Role-play discussions among people from one or several of these nations. Talk about what has changed, and what has not changed, in your life due to the nationalist movement in your country at this time.

Nonviolence: Theory and Practice

Directions: Mohandas Gandhi called for nonviolent civil disobedience in India, as expressed in the passage below. Nonviolent protest, though, sometimes was met by violence, as the eyewitness account testifies. Read these passages and then answer the questions that follow.

Mohandas Gandhi, nationalist leader

Passive [nonviolent] resistance is a method of securing rights by personal suffering. It is the reverse of resistance by arms. . . . Nonviolent non-cooperation must have its root in love. Its object should not be to punish the opponent or to inflict injury upon him. Even while non-cooperating with him, we must make him feel that in us he has a friend. We should try to reach his heart by rendering him humanitarian service wherever possible.*

---

* as quoted in Eknath Easwaran, *Gandhi the Man.* Petaluma, CA: Nilgiri Press, 1978

Webb Miller, reporter for the *New Freeman*, May 21, 1930, describing a march on salt deposits controlled by the British

[The column of protesters] approached the barbed-wire stockade. . . . The column silently ignored the warning [to disperse] and slowly walked forward. . . . Suddenly, at a word of command, scores of native police rushed upon the advancing marchers and rained blows on their heads with their steel-shod *lathis* [five-foot clubs tipped with steel]. Not one of the marchers even raised an arm to fend off the blows. They went down like ten-pins. . . . I heard the sickening whacks of the clubs on unprotected skulls. . . . Those struck down fell sprawling, unconscious or writhing in pain with fractured skulls or broken shoulders. In two or three minutes the ground was quilted with bodies.*

---

* from Webb Miller, *I Found No Peace,* London: Victor Gallancz, 1940, 1941. © The Estate of Webb Miller

1. Were the salt marches effective? If so, how did they accomplish the purpose?

2. Besides beatings like those described above, what other price did protesters pay?

3. After the first group of protesters was carried off for first-aid treatment, a second group of protesters stepped forward. Suppose you had been part of this group. Would you have stepped forward? Why or why not?

Extra Challenge: Write a letter to Gandhi suggesting alternatives to nonviolent protest that you think could be effective.

Revolution in China

Part 1 Directions: Imagine that you live in China in the 1920s. Which side would you support—the Kuomintang of Sun Yixian and Jiang Jieshi, or the Communist party of Mao Zedong? Explain your choice for each person described below.

1. A banker: _____

_____

2. A landless peasant: _____

_____

3. A business owner: _____

_____

4. An urban laborer: _____

_____

5. A landlord: _____

_____

6. A warlord: _____

_____

7. A student: _____

_____

8. An activist woman: _____

_____

9. A military officer: _____

_____

Part 2 Directions: Explain this description by Mao Zedong, in metaphor, of the Long March retreat as a victory.

> The Long March is also a seeding-machine. It has sown many seeds in 11 provinces, which will sprout, grow leaves, blossom into flowers, bear fruit, and yield a crop in future.

                                       Focus on World History: The Twentieth Century

Marxism: Theory and Practice

Directions: Karl Marx and Friedrich Engels predicted that a worldwide **proletarian** revolution would end capitalism. They express their ideas in the passages below. Communists embraced the ideas of Marx and Engels. But when Communists actually took power in Russia and China, they adapted these ideas to fit their particular situations. Read the passages from Marx and Engels. Then explain the ways in which the Communist leaders named below adapted Marxism.

Friedrich Engels, *Socialism: Utopian and Scientific*

The capitalist method of production more and more transforms the great majority of the population into proletarians. As it does so, it creates the power that, under penalty of its own destruction, is forced to accomplish this revolution. It pushes on, more and more, the transformation of the vast means of production, already socialized, into state property. In doing so, it shows itself the path to follow in order to accomplish this revolution. *The proletariat seizes the state's power and transforms the means of production, at first, into state property.**

---

* from a pamphlet published serially in *Revue Socialiste*, 1880

Karl Marx and Friedrich Engels, *The Communist Manifesto*, 1848

Not only has the bourgeoisie forged the weapons that bring death to itself; it has also called into existence the men who are to wield those weapons—the modern working class—the proletariat. . . . The proletariat will use its political supremacy to wrest, by degrees, all capital from the bourgeoisie, to centralize all instruments of production in the hands of the state, *i.e.*, of the proletariat organized as the ruling class.*

Karl Marx

---

* from Karl Marx and Friedrich Engels, *The Communist Manifesto.*

1. Lenin's adaptation of Marxism: _____

   _____

2. Stalin's adaptation of Marxism: _____

   _____

3. Mao Zedong's adaptation of Marxism: _____

   _____

"The Crisis of the Spirit"

World War I left a legacy of doubt, despair, and anxiety among many of its survivors, especially the younger generation. French author Paul Valéry expressed this in a 1919 essay titled "The Crisis of the Spirit" ("Le Crise de l'Esprit"). The new anxieties also found expression in the arts.

Directions: Read Valéry's words below. Then give specific examples of works by artists in the fields noted that express these feelings.

Paul Valéry, French writer

The storm has just ended, and yet we are as disquieted, as anxious, as if the storm were still to break upon us. Nearly all things human remain in terrible uncertainty. . . . We are almost destroyed by what is destroyed; we do not know what will come forth: still we can reasonably fear it. . . . Our fears are infinitely more precise than our hopes; we admit that the best of life is behind us, . . . but disarray and doubt are in us and with us. . . . *But among all these wounded things is the spirit. The spirit in truth is cruelly stricken.**

---

* from *The Athenaeum* (London), April 11 and May 2, 1919

1. Painting: _____

   _____

2. Music: _____

   _____

3. Poetry: _____

   _____

4. Novels: _____

   _____

"Meditation,"
René Magritte, 1937

Women's Lives

Directions: Events during the 1920s and 1930s had great impacts on women's lives in many nations. Imagine you are a woman of these times in each situation below. Describe the ways in which your life changes.

1. You are a woman in Stalinist Russia: _____
   _____

2. You are a woman in Turkey during Atatürk's time: _____
   _____

3. You are a woman in China where Mao Zedong's forces are in control: _____
   _____

4. You are a woman in Italy under Mussolini: _____
   _____

5. You are a woman in Japan: _____
   _____

6. You are a woman in India during Gandhi's campaign against the British: _____
   _____

7. You are a woman in the United States or western Europe: _____
   _____

8. You are a woman in Iran under the rule of Reza Shah Pahlavi: _____
   _____

9. You are a woman in Hitler's Germany: _____
   _____

Extra Challenge: Partner with a classmate and become "pen pals" as two women from different countries as described above. Write a series of letters describing and comparing the changes you are experiencing in your lives.

Time Line of the Russian Revolution

Directions: The Russian Revolution went through phases:

- 1905 Revolution and events that led to it
- Events between revolutions
- March 1917 Revolution and following events
- November 1917 Revolution and following events

Create a chart with a column for each of the four phases and record each event below in the appropriate column. Then, add dates and create a time line.

Bloody Sunday

Russia enters World War I.

Petrograd strike and riots

Bolshevik Revolution

New Economic Policy launches.

Tsar Nicholas and family executed

Lenin goes into exile in Europe.

Lenin dies.

Lenin returns to Russia.

First Duma meets.

Trans-Siberian railroad completed.

Rasputin is murdered.

Civil war in Russia

Tsar Nicholas abdicates.

Russian Marxists split into two factions: Mensheviks and Bolsheviks.

Kerensky establishes provisional government.

Russian empire renamed U.S.S.R.

Tsar Nicholas goes to war front to rally troops.

Treaty of Brest-Litovsk takes Russia out of World War I.

Stalin launches first Five-Year Plan.

Russo-Japanese War

The Kremlin, Moscow

The Soviet Economy

Directions: Lenin launched his New Economic Policy in 1921. It was a mixture of communism and capitalism. Stalin used several Five-Year Plans to direct the Soviet economy, beginning in 1928. Compare the features of these economic policies by completing this Venn diagram.

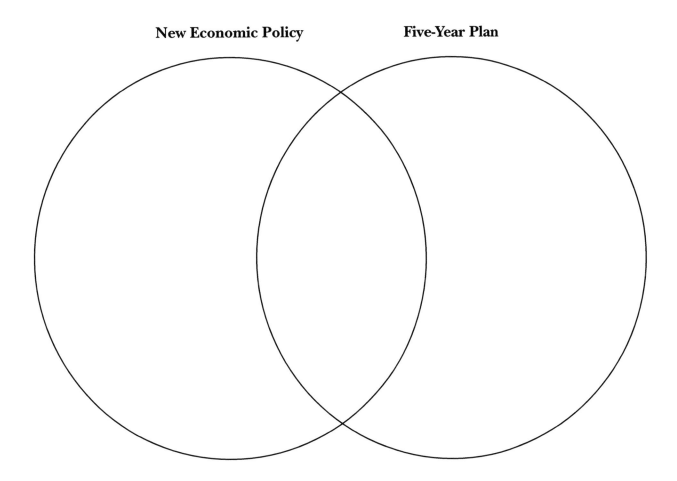

New Economic Policy   **Five-Year Plan**

Communism, Fascism, Democracy

Directions: Fill in this chart with details about communism, fascism, and democracy. The result will provide you with a handy summary of the ways in which these political systems were/are similar and different.

	Communism	Fascism	Democracy
Ideology			
Leaders/leadership			
Political party/parties			
Valued social classes			
Economic policy			
State vs. individual rights			
Foreign policy			
Role of police			

Mass Culture

Directions: Explain the elements of mass culture across national lines that are expressed in these images.

53
Focus on World History: The Twentieth Century

The Great Depression

Part 1 Directions: This diagram shows the flow of cash that brought economic recovery to Europe. Explain its elements by answering the questions.

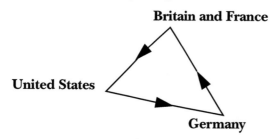

1. What cash flowed from the United States to Germany, and why?
2. What cash flowed from Germany to France and Britain, and why?
3. What cash flowed from France and Britain to the United States, and why?
4. How did the Great Depression cause this triangular flow of cash to stop? What was the effect of this stoppage?

Part 2 Directions: Add details to the elements of the economic spiral shown below to explain how each factor pushed down the economy further.

Industrial workers get higher wages.

Prices of manufactured goods _____ .

Consumers _____ .

Store owners _____ .

Factories _____ .

Workers _____ .

Factories _____ .

Workers _____ .

Extra Challenge: Construct a similar spiral for the farm economy, beginning with the factors of improved scientific farming methods and new and improved farm machinery.

Scenes of the Great Depression

Directions: The images on these pages show effects of the Great Depression in the United States. Similar effects hit people in other parts of the world as the Great Depression spread around the globe. Study each image, and then write a narrative for each. How did the tenant farmer live before the Great Depression hit? What might he have done after moving? Why did banks fail, who was affected, and in what ways?

Latin America and the United States

Directions: Latin America and the United States interacted often in the years between 1900 and the 1930s. The Latin American nations did not ask for this interaction. The United States imposed it. On your map of Latin America, locate and label the following nations and the dates of intervention. As a key to the map, fill in the information below.

1. Cuba

   Date(s) of U.S. intervention: _____

   Type of U.S. intervention/involvement:

   _____

   Reason for intervention:

   _____

2. Dominican Republic

   Date(s) of U.S. intervention: _____

   Type of U.S. intervention/involvement:

   _____

   Reason for intervention:

   _____

3. Guatemala

   Date(s) of U.S. intervention: _____

   Type of U.S. intervention/involvement:

   _____

   Reason for intervention:

   _____

4. Haiti

   Date(s) of U.S. intervention: _____

   Type of U.S. intervention/involvement:

   _____

   Reason for intervention:

   _____

5. Honduras

   Date(s) of U.S. intervention: _____

   Type of U.S. intervention/involvement:

   _____

   Reason for intervention:

   _____

6. Mexico

   Date(s) of U.S. intervention: _____

   Type of U.S. intervention/involvement:

   _____

   Reason for intervention:

   _____

7. Nicaragua

   Date(s) of U.S. intervention: _____

   Type of U.S. intervention/involvement:

   _____

   Reason for intervention:

   _____

8. Panama

   Date(s) of U.S. intervention: _____

   Type of U.S. intervention/involvement:

   _____

   Reason for intervention:

   _____

9. Puerto Rico

   Date(s) of U.S. intervention: _____

   Type of U.S. intervention/involvement:

   _____

   Reason for intervention:

   _____

10. Virgin Islands

    Date(s) of U.S. intervention: _____

    Type of U.S. intervention/involvement:

    _____

    Reason for intervention:

    _____

World War II

The objective of this unit is to help students understand the causes, course and nature, outcome, and consequences of World War II. A series of actions taken by the aggressively expansionist nations of Japan, Germany, and Italy paved the way to war during the 1930s. Leaders of the western European democracies followed a policy of appeasement in reaction to the aggression, while the United States held to a policy of isolation. Britain and France finally drew the line at Hitler's invasion of Poland, and the second global conflict of the century began in 1939. This was a truly worldwide war, with the theater in the Pacific just as important as the fighting in Europe, the Middle East, and North Africa. The Axis Powers won many victories in the first years of the war, but the tide turned in the Allies' favor in mid-1942, helped by the United States' entrance into the conflict following the Japanese attack on Pearl Harbor late in 1941. The Allies secured victory in Europe in May 1945, while the United States forced Japan to surrender in August 1945 after atomic bomb attacks on Hiroshima and Nagasaki. Destructive as World War I had been, World War II was even more so, leaving Europe in ruins. The war's end also revealed the Nazis' mass murder of Europe's Jews, as well as other "undesirables," in concentration and extermination camps. The activities of this unit are designed to draw students into a better understanding of this second great global conflict of the twentieth century.

Student Activities

Worksheet 1, Steps Toward War, presents the series of aggressive moves made by Japan, Germany, and Italy in the 1930s; students describe the response by the League of Nations and the Western democracies to each move, clearly demonstrating the ineffectiveness of the policy of appeasement.

Worksheet 2, The Munich Agreement, contrasts Hitler's statements on German expansion in *Mein Kampf* with a *Time* magazine commentary on the possibility of peace created by the Munich Agreement. Students analyze why the Western democracies adhered to a policy of appeasement in light of Hitler's clearly stated expansionist statements, and then develop alternative responses by France and Britain to Hitler's aggressive moves.

Worksheet 3, War Technology, presents four new weapons of the war—radar, sonar, aircraft carrier, and atomic bomb. Students describe each weapon and its destructive effect.

Worksheet 4, National Expansion: Two Reactions, presents photographs of two different people's crying reactions to the entrance of Nazi troops into their nations—a German Sudetan woman and a French man in Paris. Students explain why each person is crying, revealing how similar events can affect those involved in very different ways.

Worksheet 5, Women War Workers, presents two World War II propaganda posters featuring women; students explain how each one promotes a changed perception of women. The Extra Challenge invites students to read more about women's roles in World War II and then tie them to changed roles for Western women in the postwar years and decades.

Worksheet 6, The Holocaust: Why Obey? presents excerpts relating to responsibility for the Holocaust—one, from the commander of the Auschwitz concentration camp explaining why he carried out orders to exterminate Jews, and the other from a Holocaust survivor ascribing responsibility to people beyond the Nazis. Students analyze the commentaries and the question of responsibility, and consider the issue of a soldier's duty to obey orders.

Worksheet 7, The Atomic Bomb, presents elements of the debate among U.S. scientists and military and political leaders about whether or not to use the atomic bomb against Japan. Students identify the main points for and against using the bomb and then role-play a debate among contemporary scientists and planners on the issue.

Worksheet 8, War Casualties—World War II, presents country-by-country figures on military and civilian deaths in the war. Students analyze the figures by answering a series of questions and then use the figures in the chart to create a bar graph or pie chart of war casualties. The Extra Challenge invites students to compare these figures with the World War I figures on Worksheet 9, Unit 2.

World War II

The Road to War

Many people had called World War I "the war to end all wars." Certainly most people had hoped that would be true. Yet the peace agreements that ended World War I had left many problems unsolved and had even created new problems. During the 1920s, nations adjusted to the postwar changes. During the 1930s, clashes between nations began to break out again. Each clash was a step on the road to World War II.

In the 1930s, Germany and Italy were ruled by the dictators Adolf Hitler and Benito Mussolini. Japan's government was controlled by militarists. Each of these countries had a foreign policy of expansion. They made repeated acts of aggression during the 1930s. People of the Western democracies were repelled by the thought of another war. The United States held to a policy of isolation, avoiding any involvement in the affairs of Europe. Leaders of Great Britain and France followed a policy of **appeasement.** That is, they protested but gave in to the demands of the aggressors in order to keep the peace.

> The League of Nations denounced these acts of aggression. But the League had no power to act against the aggressors. In fact, when the League condemned Japan's actions in Manchuria, Japan dropped out of the League.

Japan took the first step toward war in 1931, when it invaded Manchuria, taking it from China. Other steps soon followed:

- In 1935, Germany began to rearm itself. This was a violation of the Versailles Treaty.

- In 1936, German troops moved into the Rhineland, next to France. This, too, was a treaty violation.

- Italian troops invaded Ethiopia in 1935 and made that African nation part of Italy in 1936.

- Japan's army spread out over eastern China in 1937.

- In Spain, German and Italian forces helped a right-wing general win a bloody civil war. Fighting raged from 1936 to 1939.

German moves in eastern Europe were the final steps toward war. Germany claimed a right to "living room" for its people. It also claimed a right to unite all German-speaking people. So in March 1938 Germany annexed German-speaking Austria. In September 1938, Hitler met in Munich, Germany, with the French premier and the British prime minister. They agreed to allow Hitler to annex the Sudetenland. This was the German-speaking part of Czechoslovakia.

Hitler in France

(continued)

World War II (continued)

> When he arrived home from Munich, a smiling Neville Chamberlain—the British prime minister—said that the agreement he had made with Hitler "means peace in our time." He was very wrong. British politician Winston Churchill said, "They [the British and French diplomats] had to choose between war and dishonor. They chose dishonor; they will have war." He was very right.

In September 1939, the German army marched into Poland, seizing that nation as "living room" for Germans. Britain and France finally decided they had to act. They declared war on Germany. World War II had begun.

The War Begins in Europe

World War II was a truly worldwide war. Battles in the Pacific Ocean area were as critical to the outcome as battles in Europe. So were actions in North Africa and the Soviet Union. This was a war of quick troop movements, backed up by armed war planes. It was also a war in which both sides bombed civilians.

The early years of the war brought a lot of success to the Axis Powers. Hitler's army and air force moved swiftly to take over western Poland. The Germans called this type of speedy action *blitzkrieg*, "lightning war." The Soviet Union then seized eastern Poland, three Baltic countries, and, after fierce fighting, Finland.

> In this war, the main Allies were Great Britain, France, the Soviet Union, and (from December 1941) the United States. The main Axis Powers were Germany, Italy, and Japan.

Meanwhile, British and French troops massed in France but saw no action. In April 1940, German forces suddenly invaded neutral Denmark and Norway. In May, the German *blitzkrieg* overran the Netherlands and Belgium and then poured into northern France. British troops, and some French, had to retreat across the English Channel.

> People in the Western nations called the months of quiet in the west the "phony war" or "sitzkrieg."

German troops pressed south and took Paris, the French capital, in June 1940. Hitler then launched his plan to bomb Britain into surrender. Waves of German planes dropped bombs on British cities, railroads, and factories. The period of the heaviest bombing, in 1940, was called the Battle of Britain. But fighter pilots of the British Royal Air Force downed many German planes, and Hitler ended the bombing campaign.

(continued)

World War II *(continued)*

The War Spreads

The Axis Powers also took control of Eastern Europe and the Mediterranean area. Italy took Albania in 1939. Germany invaded and took over the countries of eastern Europe in 1941. Italian and German troops also took over large parts of North Africa. (The Allies held on to most of the Middle East, plus Egypt.) In Asia, Japan took over French Indochina and the Dutch East Indies.

> Hitler's invasion of Russia was a repeat of Napoleon's big mistake. The French army suffered huge losses in 1812, when the brutal Russian winter forced the French troops to retreat.

With France under German control to the west, Hitler decided to invade the Soviet Union on the east. He thought German troops could take the U.S.S.R. in a *blitzkrieg* during the summer and fall of 1941. Millions of Russian troops died resisting the German onslaught. But the German advance stalled when a powerful Soviet ally arrived—the Russian winter. Both Russians under siege and German besiegers suffered terribly during the long, brutally cold winter.

The United States Enters the War

When the war began, the United States declared itself neutral. But most Americans favored the Allies. In early 1941, the U.S. Congress passed the Lend-Lease Act. This law allowed the sale of U.S. war materials to Britain and other nations. The United States Navy helped protect ships carrying these supplies across the Atlantic Ocean from German submarine attacks.

The United States did not like Japan's moves in Asia. So the U.S. stopped shipments of war-related raw materials to Japan. In response, Japan launched a devastating surprise air attack on the U.S. Navy base at Pearl Harbor, Hawaii, on December 7, 1941. The United States declared war on Japan. Germany and Italy—Japan's allies—declared war on the United States. The conflict now reached entirely around the globe.

The attack on Pearl Harbor

(continued)

World War II *(continued)*

The Tide Turns for the Allies

The years of war through 1941 had seen a series of Axis victories. The tide began to turn in favor of the Allies during 1942. In November of that year, Allied forces landed troops in North Africa. They drove Axis forces out of that region by May 1943. From there, they launched an invasion of Italy in July. Early in 1943, the Soviets defeated the Germans at Stalingrad. They then began driving the rest of the invading German army back west toward Germany. On the Atlantic Ocean, the Allies had new weapons—sonar and aircraft carriers. They largely quashed the power of German submarines, or U-boats.

Allied armies invaded France across the English Channel on June 4, 1944—D-Day. Soon they began to push the Germans back to Germany, as the Soviets continued their push westward. By March 1945 the Allies were in Germany. The Axis powers of Europe surrendered on May 8—V-E (Victory in Europe) Day.

Adolf Hitler committed suicide in Berlin to avoid capture by the enemy Allies. Antifascist **guerrillas** captured and executed Mussolini in Italy.

The War in the Pacific

In the months after Pearl Harbor, Japanese forces had swept across the Pacific. But the tide turned against Japan when it lost the battles of the Coral Sea and Midway in May and June 1942. U.S. forces then ejected the Japanese from a string of strategic islands in a series of fierce, bloody battles. By 1944, U.S. warplanes were bombing Japan itself.

Japan's fighting ability by now was greatly weakened. But the Japanese were still fiercely determined to resist. It seemed that only a U.S. invasion of Japan would force a Japanese surrender. American military leaders, including President Harry Truman, thought the loss of Allied life in such an invasion would be much too high. So they turned to a terrifying new weapon, the atomic bomb. The U.S. dropped a single bomb on the Japanese city of Hiroshima on August 6, 1945. It killed 80,000 people instantly. On August 9, the U.S. dropped a second bomb on the city of Nagasaki. On August 14, Japan surrendered. It signed formal surrender papers on September 1, 1945—V-J (Victory in Japan) Day. The war was over.

Allied armies invade France—D-Day

(continued)

World War II *(continued)*

The Japanese bombing of Shanghai

The Price of the War

Like World War I, World War II was extremely expensive. More than 20 million people died, both soldiers and civilians. Much of Europe was left in ruins, from land battles and extensive bombing. Millions of people were refugees. Food was scarce, and jobs were gone.

When Allied troops moved through Germany and eastern Europe, they discovered another dreadful price of the war. Adolf Hitler had focused his ethnic hatred on Jews during the 1930s. In 1941, Hitler came up with a "Final Solution" to the "Jewish problem." All Jews in Germany, and in German-occupied lands, were to be killed. Nazi police and soldiers rounded up Jews from all across Europe. They were shipped in railroad cattle cars to concentration camps in eastern Germany and Poland. There millions of Jews—and other people Hitler considered "inferior"—died by poison gas. Their bodies were burned in huge ovens that

ran day and night. This mass murder became known as the Holocaust.

As the war ended, Allied troops found the Nazi concentration camps. People outside Germany were shocked. Many civilians had died in the war because of bombings and battles near their homes. But the planned killing of most of an ethnic group—**genocide**—was not an accepted part of war. So Nazi leaders were tried and convicted of war crimes in a special court at Nuremberg, Germany. Japanese wartime leaders were also tried and convicted for war crimes. Their guilt was for actions against civilians in the Asian countries that Japan had conquered.

Concentration-camp survivors

When World War I began, the nations of Western Europe were the most important and powerful countries of the world. By the end of the Second World War, two different nations commanded the scene: the United States and the Soviet Union. Their clashing interests would dominate world affairs in the postwar world.

Steps Toward War

Directions: Japan, Germany, and Italy made a series of aggressive moves against other regions during the 1930s. Each move was a large step toward the outbreak of World War II. For each step listed below, describe the response by the League of Nations and Western democracies. What pattern emerges from your answers?

1. **September 1931:** Japan seizes Manchuria.

   Response: _____

   _____

2. **March 1935:** Germany announces it will ignore Versailles Treaty limitations on size of its army.

   Response: _____

   _____

3. **October 1935:** Italy invades Ethiopia.

   Response: _____

   _____

4. **March 1936:** Germany occupies Rhineland, in violation of Versailles Treaty.

   Response: _____

   _____

5. **July 1937:** Japan invades China.

   Response: _____

   _____

6. **March 1938:** Germany annexes Austria.

   Response: _____

   _____

7. **September 1938:** Germany takes the Sudetenland.

   Response: _____

   _____

8. **March 1939:** Germany takes Czechoslovakia.

   Response: _____

   _____

9. **April 1939:** Italy seizes Albania.

   Response: _____

   _____

10. **September 1939:** Germany invades Poland.

    Response: _____

    _____

The Munich Agreement

Directions: British Prime Minister Neville Chamberlain said that the Munich Agreement had achieved "peace in our time." Great Britain and France achieved this "peace" by agreeing to Hitler's aggressive moves. Assess this policy of appeasement by analyzing the following readings and answering the questions that follow.

Adolf Hitler, from *Mein Kampf*, 1927

The National Socialist movement must strive to eliminate the disproportion between our population and our area—viewing this latter as a source of food as well as a basis for power politics. . . . We National Socialists must hold unflinchingly to our aim in foreign policy, namely, to secure for the German people the land and soil to which they are entitled on this earth. . . . State boundaries are made by man and changed by man. . . . Germany will either be a world power or there will be no Germany. And for world power she needs that expansion.*

* from Adolf Hitler, *Mein Kampf,* translated by Rolph Manheim. Boston: Houghton Mifflin, 1943, 1971

Time magazine, October 10, 1938

The crisis proved . . . that modern communication and enlightenment . . . reduce the chances of an outbreak of war. For the first time in history, a major conflict had been settled by talking instead of shooting first. And, while [many people] deplored the dismemberment of central Europe's one island of democracy and were saddened for the painful uprooting of the minorities which will leave the ceded territories, realists took heart from one fact. . . . The Czechoslovakia rape had at least set a precedent, which might flower into a great influence for peace, for aggressors being persuaded to follow legal-diplomatic forms.*

* © 1938 *Time* magazine

1. In view of Hitler's statements on expansion, why would the Western democracies adhere to a policy of appeasement?

    _____

    _____

    _____

2. Develop an alternative response by France and Britain to Hitler's aggressive moves. Present your response as a position paper to be discussed at the highest levels of your government.

War Technology

Directions: World War II was the most destructive war in history. The mayhem was enhanced by advances in military technology. Describe each new war technology and tell how it made World War II so much more destructive.

1. Radar

   Description: _____

   _____

   Effect: _____

   _____

4. Sonar

   Description: _____

   _____

   Effect: _____

   _____

2. Aircraft carrier

   Description: _____

   _____

   Effect: _____

   _____

3. Atomic bomb

   Description: _____

   _____

   Effect: _____

   _____

Extra Challenge: Explain how improvements in aircraft, tanks, and submarines made the technologies of warfare more deadly in World War II as compared with technologies in World War I.

National Expansion: Two Reactions

Directions: Moves to expand a nation's territory most often are met with very different responses by those involved. Explain the reactions you see in these two photographs from World War II.

1. This is a German Sudeten woman reacting to German troops marching into Czechoslovakia's Sudeten region in 1938. Why do you think she is she crying?

2. This is a French man reacting to German troops marching into Paris in 1940. Why do you think he is crying?

Women War Workers

Directions: Women in Europe and the United States played a large and an important role in World War II. This role changed women's views of themselves, their abilities, and their place in society. Study these World War II propaganda posters, and explain how each one promotes a changed perception of women.

1.

2.

Extra Challenge: Read more about women's roles in World War II. Then create a report that explains how Western women's roles in World War II affected their roles in Western society in the years and decades after World War II ended.

The Holocaust: Why Obey?

Directions: The German Nazis murdered millions of Jews in World War II death camps built for this purpose. Who carried out this policy, and why? Who bears responsibility? Develop answers to these questions by reading these excerpts and responding to the questions that follow.

Rudolf Höss, commander of the Auschwitz concentration camp

I personally never hated Jews. I considered them to be the enemy of our nation. . . . Himmler gave me the order personally in the summer of 1941 to prepare a place for mass killings [of Jews] and then carry it out. . . . At the time I wasted no thoughts about it. I had received an order; I had to carry it out. I could not allow myself to form an opinion as to whether this mass extermination of the Jews was necessary or not. . . . Since the Führer himself had ordered "The Final Solution of the Jewish Question," there was no second guessing.*

---

* from Rudolf Höss, *Death Dealer, The Memoirs of the SS Kommandant at Auschwitz,* Steven Paskuly, ed. Amherst, NY: Prometheus Books, 1992

Robert Fisch, Jewish Hungarian survivor of the Holocaust

Responsibility is a very complicated issue. Eichmann was originally assigned to make emigration possible for the Hungarian Jews, for $400 each in trucks or other merchandise. But no country would "buy" the Jews. You cannot blame a Hitler when millions of people were taken by trains, "assisted" by local guards and train engineers. Roosevelt knew exactly what was happening, so why were the trains not bombed, to stop the concentration camp activities? . . . We should raise our voices when a mass extermination is taking place.*

---

* from *Witnesses to the Holocaust,* Jewish Community Relations Council/Anti-Defamation League of Minnesota and the Dakotas, edited by Rhoda G. Levin. Boston: Twayne Publishers, 1990

1. Why did Höss arrange for and carry out the mass killings of Jews? Do you think his justification is reasonable, or unreasonable, partly or in full?

2. Who else might bear responsibility for the mass killings of the Holocaust, according to Fisch? Do you agree or disagree with him?

3. Soldiers must carry out orders. How could a soldier refuse an order? What consequences would he or she face? Describe a situation in which a soldier is justified in refusing an order.

4. "My country, right or wrong" is an old patriotic saying. Do you think it is a valid basis for action and decision making? Under all circumstances? Why or why not?

The Atomic Bomb

Scientists and military and political leaders debated in depth whether or not to use the atomic bomb against Japan. This debate still relates to today's world of nuclear weapons. This page and the next present major points made at the time about this issue.

U.S. scientists, pro-bomb use, 1945

Are not the men of the fighting forces who are risking their lives for the nation entitled to the weapons which have been designed? Are we to go on shedding American blood when we have available means to a steady victory? [petition signed by seventy U.S. scientists]

It is hard to imagine anything [worse] than the devastation of the eastern coastal cities of Japan by fire bombs; a more fiendish hell than the inferno of blazing Tokyo is beyond the pale of conception. Then why do we attempt to draw the line of morality here, when it is a question of degree, not a question of kind? [scientist Evan J. Young of Clinton Laboratories]*

---

* as quoted in David McCullough, *Truman.* New York: Simon & Schuster, 1992

U.S. scientists' warning about bomb use, Franck Report, 1945

We think that the question of the use of the very first available atomic bombs in the Japanese war should be weighed very carefully. . . . If we consider international agreement on total prevention of nuclear warfare as the paramount objective, and believe that it can be achieved, this kind of introduction of atomic weapons to the world may easily destroy all our chances of success. . . . The military advantages and the saving of American lives achieved by the sudden use of atomic bombs against Japan may be outweighed by the ensuing loss of confidence and by a wave of horror and repulsion sweeping over the rest of the world and perhaps even dividing public opinion at home. . . .

From this point of view, a demonstration of the new weapon might best be made, before the eyes of representatives of all the United Nations, on the desert or a barren island. [Then] America could say to the world, "You see what sort of a weapon we had but did not use. We are ready to renounce its use in the future if other nations join us in this renunciation and agree to the establishment of an efficient international control."*

---

* from recommendations submitted to the U.S. government by the Committee on the Social and Political Implications of Atomic Energy, a group of Chicago-based scientists chaired by James Franck

(continued)

The Atomic Bomb *(continued)*

Henry L. Stimson, U.S. Secretary of War, article in *Harper's Magazine*, 1947

[A study committee rejected an advance demonstration of the bomb.] [It was] not regarded as likely to be effective in compelling a surrender of Japan, and [it] involved serious risks. . . . [We could not be sure] that any given bomb was certain to explode when dropped from an airplane. . . . A dud was a real possibility. [And] we had no bombs to waste. . . .

I felt that to extract a genuine surrender from the Emperor and his military advisers, they must be administered a tremendous shock which would carry convincing proof of our power to destroy the Empire. Such an effective shock would save many times the number of lives, both American and Japanese, that it would cost.*

---

* © 1947 *Harper's Magazine*

U.S. Strategic Bomb Survey, 1946

On 9 March 1945, a basic revision in the methods of B-29 attack was instituted. It was decided to bomb the four principal Japanese cities at night. . . . The chosen areas were saturated. Fifteen square miles of Tokyo's most densely populated areas were burned to the ground. . . . A striking aspect of the air attack was the pervasiveness with which its impact on morale blanketed Japan. Roughly one quarter of all people in cities fled or were evacuated, and these evacuees, who themselves were of singularly low morale, helped spread discouragement and disaffection for the war throughout the islands. . . . In the final analysis the Japanese military machine had lost its purpose when it could no longer protect the Japanese people from destruction by air attack. General Takashima . . . stated [after the war] that surrender had become unavoidable.*

---

* from *United States Strategic Bombing Survey (Pacific War)*. Washington, D.C.: U.S. Government Printing Office, 1946

Directions: In chart form, identify the main points for and against using the atomic bomb against Japan. Then role-play a debate among concerned scientists and military planners about whether or not to use the atomic bomb against Japan. Take into account these factors:

1. The Allied military position in the Pacific in 1945

2. Estimated military and civilian casualties in a prolonged war and an Allied invasion of Japan

3. Long-term consequences as understood in 1945

4. Japanese surrender overtures in 1945

5. The probability of the Soviet Union entering the war against Japan

War Casualties—World War II

Directions: Given below are estimated numbers of military personnel and civilians who died in World War II, broken down by country. First, answer the questions about the figures. Then, use the figures to create a bar graph or pie chart of war casualties.

DEATHS IN WORLD WAR II		
Country	Military deaths	Civilian deaths
Soviet Union	7,500,000	15,000,000
Germany	2,850,000	500,000[a]
Japan	1,500,000	300,000
China	500,000	1,000,000
Great Britain	400,000	65,000
United States	290,000	[b]
France	210,000	110,000
Italy	80,000	100,000
Others	1,500,000	16,000,000[c]

[a] Jewish Holocaust deaths are included in "Others."   [c] Includes victims of Jewish Holocaust, Poles, and others

[b] Figures are not available; losses were quite small.

1. Which country had the greatest loss of life? _____

2. How many military deaths did the Axis Powers included in the figures above suffer?
   _____

3. How many military deaths did the Allied countries included in the figures above suffer?
   _____

4. Which country had the greatest number of civilian deaths? _____
   What accounts for this? _____

5. Which country had the second-greatest number of civilian deaths? _____
   What accounts for this? _____

6. Which country had very few civilian deaths? _____
   What accounts for this? _____

Extra Challenge: Compare the figures shown here with the World War I casualty figures on Worksheet 9, Unit 2. Note differences between the two wars for Great Britain, France, the United States, Germany (Germany and Austria-Hungary for World War I), and the Soviet Union (Russia for World War I). Explain what may account for the differences.

Postwar to Millennium

The objective of this unit is to help students better understand events of the second half of the twentieth century, including the Cold War, the process of colonial independence, the intractable Arab-Israeli conflict, developments in Asia and Latin America, and changes in communist China and the former Soviet Union. The United States and the U.S.S.R., allies during World War II, emerged as the world's two postwar superpowers, with very different agendas. At home, the two engaged in a costly arms race, while abroad they clashed repeatedly while trying to promote their interests in other nations. This Cold War dominated world affairs until the Soviet Union dissolved in the 1990s in the wake of attempts to establish elements of a market economy and allow criticism of the government. At the same time, colonies in Asia, Africa, and the Middle East gained their independence from European countries and greatly swelled the ranks of the world's nations. Many former colonies struggled to cope with the need to industrialize, establish modern education and governmental systems, and blend competing ethnic and religious groups. In recent years, several Southeast Asian nations emerged as economic powerhouses. Postwar Japan refocused its energies on building its industrial might, while China built its own version of a communist state. Latin American nations struggled with high debt and frequent political turnovers. The activities of this unit are designed to draw students into a better understanding of these most recent decades in world history.

Student Activities

Worksheet 1, Cold War Origins, presents an assessment by a Soviet diplomat of U.S. intentions toward the U.S.S.R. and a similar assessment by a U.S. diplomat of Soviet intentions toward the United States. Students analyze the assessments, judge their accuracy, and consider how acceptance of them promoted the development of the Cold War.

Worksheet 2, U.S. Cold War Policies, presents brief descriptions of four U.S. Cold War policy variations—containment, brinkmanship, the domino theory, and détente. Students name each one, describe it in their own words, and give examples of each in action.

Worksheet 3, The Cold War Around the World, uses mapping to familiarize students with the extent of Cold War "hot spots" around the world. Students give the date and a brief description of each event on the worksheet to create a key to their map.

Worksheet 4, The Arab-Israeli Conflict: Origins, presents the basic Arab and Israeli statements about their right to Palestine, from the 1940s. Students analyze the basis of each group's assertion of right, and attempt to formulate a way to resolve the conflict.

Worksheet 5, Africa: Paths to Nationhood, is an exercise in which students match listed names of African nations with descriptions of the national sequence of events following independence, emphasizing the many different paths these nations have followed. The Extra Challenge asks students to report in depth on one of these nations.

Worksheet 6, Protest: Nonviolent and Violent, contrasts Martin Luther King, Jr.'s call for nonviolent direct action to secure black rights with Nelson Mandela's explanation of why his nationalist group adopted a policy of sabotage. Students construct arguments for or against applying Mandela's tactics to the U.S. situation, or King's tactics to the South African situation, assessing possible effectiveness in each case.

Worksheet 7, Postwar Latin America, presents Spanish terms that relate to various aspects of and situations in Latin America in the latter half of the twentieth century; students explain each term.

Worksheet 8, Communist Policy Shifts, presents Deng Xiaoping's and Mikhail Gorbachev's descriptions of changes they made, introducing some noncommunist elements to Chinese and Soviet life. Students analyze the changes and their effects, guided by a series of questions. The Extra Challenge invites students to develop alternative but practical approaches for either country that might produce different results from those that actually occurred.

Worksheet 9, East and Southeast Asia, uses mapping to familiarize students with the nations of this region while they record each date of full independence, capital, and per capita income on the worksheet. The Extra Challenge asks students to construct a bar graph to show discrepancies in per capita income among these nations.

Worksheet 10, Nationalist Leaders of Asia and Africa, is a matching activity in which students link listed names of nationalist leaders with descriptions of them. The Extra Challenge invites students to write a biography of any one of the listed leaders.

Kenyatta Conference Center, Kenya, Africa

Postwar to Millennium

Postwar Recovery in Europe

Europe was in ruins at the end of World War II. Europeans needed a lot of help to get back on their feet. U.S. Secretary of State George Marshall developed a way to provide that help. Under the Marshall Plan, the United States gave massive economic aid that funded a long-term recovery. It was a great success in western Europe, where democratic nations regained strength and also provided much-needed markets for U.S. goods.

Eastern Europe followed a different course. Soviet troops had occupied most of Eastern Europe when they drove the Germans out toward the end of the war. After the war was over, the U.S.S.R. kept control over these countries, which became Soviet **satellites.** They remained separate nations, but they were completely dominated by the U.S.S.R. Each nation's economy and government ran the way the Soviet Union directed them to run.

> Poland, Hungary, Romania, Bulgaria, Czechoslovakia, and Albania all became Soviet satellites. Yugoslavia was also communist. But its dictator, Marshal Tito, kept the country only loosely allied with the U.S.S.R.

The Cold War

Two superpowers dominated the postwar world until the 1990s—the Soviet Union and the United States. These two nations were very different. The United States was an open democracy. The Soviet Union was a communist state run by a dictator. Their goals clashed. The United States wanted countries around the world to become or remain democratic. The Soviet Union wanted the world's nations to become communist. It backed communist movements in any country wherever it could. The United States, in return, backed anticommunists around the globe.

This U.S.-Soviet struggle was called the **Cold War,** because U.S.-Soviet armies didn't actually fight armed battles against one another. Both nations had atomic, and then nuclear, weapons. If they fought a direct war against one another, each nation could be destroyed. So instead, the two superpowers fought each other indirectly. They used the "cold" weapons of money and political support to gain other nations as allies.

> U.S.-Soviet competition even extended into outer space. Each nation tried to outdo the other in space technology and exploration.

Cold War tensions broke into full crises in many areas of the world. Problems eased after the Soviet Union adopted a policy of "peaceful coexistence" in the later 1950s. Still, "hot" wars were fought in Korea in the 1950s and Vietnam in the 1960s and 1970s.

(continued)

Postwar to Millennium *(continued)*

Colonies and Independence

Many areas of Asia, Africa, and the Middle East were still colonies in the 1930s. World War II gave new fuel to nationalist movements in these colonies. Native peoples saw white colonial powers defeated. Colonial soldiers returned with a strong sense that they had now earned the right to self-rule. Most colonial powers realized they no longer had the strength or finances to hold on to overseas empires. So the late 1950s and the 1960s saw the dismantling of those wide-ranging systems of colonies.

Africa

At the end of World War II, the vast continent of Africa was almost entirely controlled by Western imperial nations. By the mid-1960s, only a few African nations remained colonies. The rest had become independent in rapid order. The process began in the late 1950s. Some of these nations gained independence with little trouble. Others had to fight hard for freedom. Problems that many newly independent African nations faced included these:

- National boundaries that included a mix of many different people. They had different languages, different customs, and often long-standing conflicts.

- Economies based on subsistence farming and almost no manufacturing.

- Few educated people trained in running a modern government.

Most newly independent African governments turned to forms of socialism to deal with these problems. Democracy on the Western model most often broke down. Most nations turned to one-person or one-party rule. The challenge to change poor, divided countries into modern, industrial, unified nations continued through the twentieth century.

Asia

India's nationalist movement was split between two major religious groups, Hindus and Muslims. They could not agree to share an India free of British colonial rule. So independence in 1948 created two new nations: India (mostly Hindu) and Pakistan (mostly Muslim). These two peoples fought bitterly along their shared border area of Kashmir, a fight that continues today. Because of these conflicts, both nations have spent heavily on their military forces. This has left fewer resources to address the problems of extreme overpopulation and widespread poverty in both countries.

> The military clashes between India and Pakistan are especially dangerous because both nations have nuclear weapons.

(continued)

Postwar to Millennium *(continued)*

> East Pakistan became a separate nation, Bangladesh, in 1971.

U.S. occupation forces controlled Japan after the war. Under U.S. direction, Japan became a democracy. It became fully independent again in 1952. The postwar treaty had disarmed Japan, so it was free to devote all its resources to domestic priorities. Japan's economy grew steadily. It has become a major exporter of consumer goods, such as electronics and automobiles.

When World War II ended, the communists and nationalists in China resumed their civil war. The communists, led by Mao Zedong, won. They had gained the backing of China's vast peasant population. Headed by Mao, the Communist party controlled all aspects of Chinese life. The communist leaders built up heavy industries and organized farms into large collectives and communes. They also aggressively pushed the spread of communism abroad. During the 1990s, China opened to noncommunist economic forms and contact. But it stayed closed to political change and dissent.

In Southeast Asia, former colonies emerged as independent nations. The region also became a field of Cold War battle, especially in Vietnam and Laos. In the 1980s and 1990s four Southeast Asian nations had such robust economies that they became known as the "four tigers." The "tigers" were South Korea, Taiwan, Hong Kong, and Singapore.

> Southeast Asia includes the countries of Vietnam, Laos, Cambodia, Burma, Thailand, Malaysia, Singapore, Indonesia, and the Philippines.

Middle East

The Middle East, too, saw independent nations emerge from colonies after World War II. The region was also a focus of Cold War rivalry between the United States and the U.S.S.R. Its vast oil reserves give it great strategic value.

> Arab nations of the Middle East include Iraq, Syria, Lebanon, Jordan, and Saudi Arabia. Turkey and Iran are non-Arab Middle Eastern nations.

The region has been a center of conflict for decades. Israel and its Arab neighbors have fought four wars to date, with Israel winning each one. Efforts to resolve the Israeli-Palestinian conflict have not yet been successful. Lebanon broke into civil war during the 1970s. Iran and Iraq fought a war against each other in the 1980s. In the Persian Gulf war of 1990, a U.S.-led coalition forced invading Iraq out of Kuwait.

(continued)

Postwar to Millennium *(continued)*

Latin America

After World War II, Latin American nations continued to face many common problems. Some countries relied on just one cash crop for most of their income. Many nations had little industry and little money to build industry. They borrowed money from the World Bank and foreign investors to meet their needs. Their economies became overburdened with foreign debt.

Economic problems brought political instability. The **coup**—a sudden overthrow of a government by a small group that seizes power—became a common feature of Latin American politics. Often, a military group, called a **junta,** would overthrow an elected government. This was most likely when a democratic government seemed to favor the common people rather than the wealthy elite. By the end of the twentieth century, stable democracy had become more common.

> The Cuban missile crisis of 1962 nearly brought on World War III. U.S. President Kennedy demanded that the Soviets remove their nuclear missiles from Cuba. U.S. Navy ships prepared to block missile-carrying Soviet ships. The world held its breath until the Soviets backed off and agreed to U.S. demands.

In 1959, rebels led by Fidel Castro overthrew the dictator of Cuba. Castro then set up Latin America's only communist government. Castro developed close ties to the Soviet Union. In response, the United States stopped all trade with Cuba and broke off diplomatic relations. The trade embargo has remained in effect ever since, despite growing calls to end it.

The United States

U.S. foreign policy focused on the Cold War into the 1990s. That policy found a new focus after September 11, 2001. On that date, terrorists flew jetliners into New York's World Trade Center and Washington's Pentagon. Another hijacked jet crashed in a field in Pennsylvania when passengers took on the terrorists. In response, U.S. President Bush declared a global "war on terror." Its first phase was a military campaign against the terror network al-Qaida and its supporters in Afghanistan.

(continued)

Postwar to Millennium *(continued)*

On the domestic scene, the civil rights movement of the 1960s ended **segregation** and secured many legal rights for black people. Widespread protests against the Vietnam War caused turmoil in the late 1960s and early 1970s. The 1980s and 1990s brought economic boom times, followed by **recessions.** Concerns about domestic security and **terrorism** have loomed large since "9/11."

The Soviet Union and Eastern Europe

The Cold War ended suddenly in 1991 when the Soviet Union unexpectedly collapsed. A new Soviet leader, Mikhail Gorbachev, began a policy of reform in 1985. He called for *glasnost,* or openness—free discussion of the Soviet Union's problems. He also urged *perestroika,* a restructuring of the economy and government. He allowed some free enterprise and loosened central control.

These changes brought economic woes and political turmoil at home. Abroad, glasnost encouraged Soviet satellites and republics to break away from the U.S.S.R. The Baltic republics regained their independence in 1991. The eastern European satellites broke out soon after. By the end of 1991, the rest of the Soviet republics had left the union and the U.S.S.R. ceased to exist. During the 1990s, Russia continued to struggle through the painful changeover to a market economy.

Street market in Russia

Cold War Origins

Directions: The U.S.-Soviet alliance fell apart at the end of World War II. The two superpowers developed foreign policies toward one another based on mutual fear and distrust. These policies sprang from each nation's analysis of the other nation's intentions. A Soviet and a U.S. diplomat each wrote very influential assessments, which shaped these two policies. Read these excerpts and analyze them guided by the questions that follow.

Nikolai Novikov, Soviet ambassador to the United States, 1946 cable to Moscow

The foreign policy of the United States, which reflects the imperialist tendencies of the American monopolistic capital, is characterized in the postwar period by a striving for world supremacy. . . . For this purpose broad plans for expansion have been developed and are being implemented through diplomacy and the establishment of a system of naval and air bases stretching far beyond the boundaries of the United States, through the arms race, and through the creation of ever newer types of weapons. . . . Careful note should be taken of the fact that the preparation by the United States for a future war is being conducted with the prospect of war against the Soviet Union, which in the eyes of American imperialists is the main obstacle in the path of the United States to world domination.*

---

* from *Origins of the Cold War: The Novikov, Kennan, and Roberts 'Long' Telegrams of 1946*. Kenneth M. Jensen, editor. Copyright 1993 © by the Endowment of the United States Institute of Peace. Used with permission by the United States Institute of Peace, Washington, D.C.

George Kennan, U.S. diplomat in Moscow, 1946 telegram to Washington

What we may expect of basic Soviet policies: (a) To undermine general political and strategic potential of major western policies; to disrupt national self-confidence, to hamstring national defense measures, to increase social and industrial unrest, to stimulate all forms of disunity; . . . (c) Where individual governments stand in the path of Soviet purposes, pressure will be brought for their removal from office; . . . (d) In foreign countries, to work toward destruction of all forms of personal independence; . . . (e) Everything possible will be done to set major Western Powers against each other.*

---

* from *Foreign Relations of the United States, 1946*, Vol. VI. Washington, D.C.: U.S. Government Printing Office, 1969

1. What actions does the United States plan to take around the world, according to Novikov? How accurate is Novikov's assessment, in your opinion?

2. What actions does the Soviet Union plan to take around the world, according to Kennan? How accurate is Kennan's assessment, in your opinion?

3. How would acceptance of these assessments promote the development of the Cold War?

Extra Challenge: Imagine you are a Soviet or an American diplomat of the 1940s. Write your own assessment/analysis of U.S. or Soviet goals and intentions that takes a much less hard-line view than does Novikov or Kennan.

U.S. Cold War Policies

Directions: The United States adopted several policy variations during the Cold War. Name each one that is described below, explain it and how it fit into the U.S. Cold War era, and give a specific example of the policy as it was put into practice during the Cold War.

1. "It must be the policy of the United States to support free people who are resisting attempted subjugation by armed minorities or by outside pressures."

   Term for policy: _____

   Description: _____

   _____

   Example of policy in effect: _____

   _____

2. "If attacked, the United States will retaliate instantly by means and at places of our own choosing."

   Term for policy: _____

   Description: _____

   _____

   Example of policy in effect: _____

   _____

3. "If South Vietnam should fall to Communist control, Laos would almost certainly come under North Vietnamese domination, Cambodia would accept Communist China's domination, Thailand would become very shaky, and Malaysia, the same."

   Term for policy: _____

   Description: _____

   _____

   Example of policy in effect: _____

   _____

4. "The United States will deal with the U.S.S.R. in a practical, flexible way, rather than through direct confrontation."

   Term for policy: _____

   Description: _____

   _____

   Example of policy in effect: _____

   _____

The Cold War Around the World

Directions: On your map of the world, locate and label the following Cold War "hot spots." These were places where Cold War tensions erupted into armed conflict or near-conflict. Fill in the date and a brief description of each incident below as a key to your map.

1. Cuba
   Date: _____
   Event: _____
   _____

2. Nicaragua
   Date: _____
   Event: _____
   _____

3. El Salvador
   Date: _____
   Event: _____
   _____

4. Greece
   Date: _____
   Event: _____
   _____

5. Turkey
   Date: _____
   Event: _____
   _____

6. Germany (Berlin)
   Date: _____
   Event: _____
   _____

7. Israel/Arab neighbors
   Date: _____
   Event: _____
   _____

8. Vietnam
   Date: _____
   Event: _____
   _____

9. Korea
   Date: _____
   Event: _____
   _____

10. Afghanistan
    Date: _____
    Event: _____
    _____

11. U.S.S.R.
    Date: _____
    Event: _____
    _____

12. Angola
    Date: _____
    Event: _____
    _____

The Arab-Israeli Conflict: Origins

Directions: During World War I, Great Britain made two contradictory promises about lands it controlled in the Middle East. Britain promised Arabs an independent state (which would include Palestine) in return for their fighting the Turks. Britain also promised **Zionists** that it would support "establishment in Palestine of a national home for the Jewish people." Arabs and Jews both felt entitled to Palestine, as expressed by the following statements. Read the statements and answer the questions that follow.

Arab statement to Anglo-American Commission on Palestine, 1946

The whole Arab people is unalterably opposed to the attempt to impose Jewish immigration and settlement upon it, and ultimately to establish a Jewish State in Palestine. Its opposition is based primarily upon right. The Arabs of Palestine are descendants of the indigenous inhabitants of the country, who have been in occupation of it since the beginning of history; they cannot agree that it is right to subject an indigenous population against its will to alien immigrants, whose claim is based upon a historical connection which ceased effectively many centuries ago. Moreover, they form the majority of the population; as such they cannot submit to a policy of immigration which if pursued for long will turn them from a majority into a minority in an alien state; and they claim the democratic right of a majority to make its own decisions in matters of urgent national concern.

Declaration of the State of Israel, 1948

The Land of Israel was the birthplace of the Jewish people. Here their spiritual, religious, and national identity was formed. Here they achieved independence and created a culture of national and universal significance. Here they wrote and gave the Bible to the world. Exiled from the Land of Israel, the Jewish people remained faithful to it in all the countries of their dispersion, never ceasing to pray and hope for their return and the restoration of their national freedom. Impelled by this historic association, Jews strove throughout the centuries to go back to the land of their fathers and regain their statehood. In recent decades they returned in masses. . . . The Balfour Declaration . . . and . . . the Mandate of the League of Nations . . . gave explicit international recognition to the historic connection of the Jewish people with Palestine and their right to reconstitute their National Home.

---

1. Why do Arabs claim a right to Palestine?

2. Why do Jews claim a right to Palestine?

3. How would you reconcile these two claims?

Africa: Paths to Nationhood

Directions: Most African nations gained independence in the second half of the twentieth century. They followed several paths to independence and found various ways to unify and rule their nations. Match each nation listed below with the correct description of the national sequence of events. A description may be used more than once.

Algeria	Kenya	South Africa
Angola	Mozambique	Sudan
Congo/Zaire	Namibia	Tanzania
Ghana	Nigeria	Uganda
		Zimbabwe/Southern Rhodesia

1. White-minority rule with violent protests and guerrilla warfare, followed by black majority rule:

   _____

2. Long war for independence, followed by military rule, then civil war: _____

3. Long guerrilla war for independence, then elected government: _____

4. Guerrilla war for independence, then long civil war: _____

5. Guerrilla warfare, then independence, then elected government with one-party rule:

   _____

6. Peaceful independence, then elected government with one-party rule: _____

7. Peaceful independence, then shifts between elected civilian governments and military rule:

   _____

8. Peaceful independence, elected government, civil war, military rule, democracy, military rule:

   _____

9. Sudden independence, civil war, long-term military dictator: _____

10. Peaceful independence, elected government, then long-term brutal military rule:

    _____

11. Peaceful independence, then shifts between elected civilian governments and military rule, then ongoing civil war:

    _____

Extra Challenge: Choose one of these nations and report in depth on its path to independence and its nation-building experience up to the present time.

Protest: Nonviolent and Violent

Nelson Mandela of South Africa and Martin Luther King, Jr. of the United States devoted themselves to securing rights for their fellow black citizens. They advocated different tactics at different times, as expressed in the statements below.

Protest tactics advocated by Martin Luther King, Jr.*

- We reject the use of violence.
- We call for nonviolent direct action, such as marches and sit-ins.
- These actions create an atmosphere of crisis and tension, and dramatize the issue.
- The crisis, tension, and drama force the community to confront the issue and to begin to negotiate.
- Without the use of nonviolent direct action, we will make no progress toward our goals.

---

* as expressed in King's "A Letter from a Birmingham Jail" to leading clergymen of Alabama, April 1963

Protest tactics advocated by Nelson Mandela*

- Government policy became so oppressive, the African people were sure to turn to violence.
- The government had banned all legal ways of protesting the practice of white supremacy.
- Only violence remained as a means of protest.
- Responsible leadership was needed to channel and control this violence.
- Four forms of violence were possible: sabotage, guerrilla warfare, terrorism, and open revolution.
- We chose sabotage because it did not involve loss of life and did not further damage race relations.
- Sabotage attacks inspire our people and provide an outlet for those who call for violent action.

---

* as expressed in Mandela's defense statement at his trial for treason, April 1964

Directions: Construct an argument for or against applying Mandela's tactics to the U.S. situation, or King's tactics to the South African situation. Do you think Mandela's tactics would be more effective, or less effective, than King's in the U.S. situation? Do you think King's tactics would be more or less effective than Mandela's in the South African situation?

Postwar Latin America

Directions: The Spanish terms below relate to various aspects of conditions and situations in Latin America during the second half of the twentieth century. Explain each term.

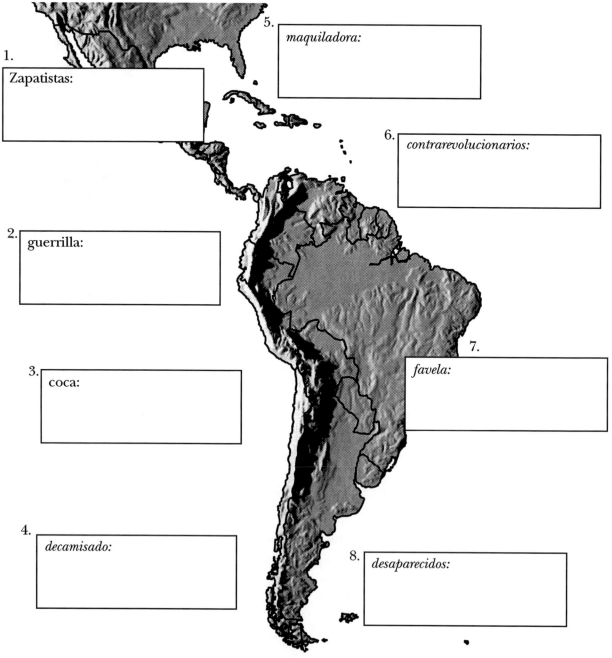

5.
maquiladora:

1.
Zapatistas:

6.
contrarevolucionarios:

2. guerrilla:

3. coca:

7.
favela:

4.
decamisado:

8.
desaparecidos:

Communist Policy Shifts

Directions: Communist leaders in both the U.S.S.R. and China shifted their policies in the 1980s. They introduced some noncommunist elements to Soviet and Chinese life, as they explain below. Read the passages and answer the questions that follow.

Deng Xiaoping on China's policy

We allow the development of individual economy, of joint ventures with both Chinese and foreign investment and of enterprises wholly owned by foreign businessmen, but socialist public ownership will always remain predominant.

Firm measures must be taken against any [dissident] who creates trouble at Tiananmen Square. . . . We cannot do without dictatorship. We must not only affirm the need for it but exercise it when necessary. . . . If we take no action and back down, we shall only have more trouble down the road.*

---

* from Deng Xiaoping [Zedong], *Fundamental Issues in Present-Day China.* Beijing: Foreign Languages Press, 1987

Mikhail Gorbachev on Soviet policy

Perestroika means mass initiative. It is the comprehensive development, encouragement of initiative and creative endeavor, improved order and discipline, more *glasnost*, criticism, and self-criticism in all spheres of our society. It is utmost respect for the individual and consideration for personal dignity. Perestroika is the . . . revival and development of the principles of democratic centralism in running the national economy.*

---

* from Mikhail Gorbachev, *Perestroika.* New York: Harper/Collins Publishers, 1987

1. What noncommunist elements does Deng allow?

2. What noncommunist elements does Gorbachev allow?

3. What limits on openness does Deng insist on? How does this compare with Gorbachev's approach?

4. What results did these changes produce in China and the U.S.S.R.?

Extra Challenge: Develop different but practical approaches for either country that might produce results different from those that actually occurred.

East and Southeast Asia

Directions: Trace the changes in postwar Asia by filling in the information for the nations listed below. For "date," record the date of the nation's full independence. "PCI" stands for "per capita income." Then locate and label each nation on your map of East and Southeast Asia.

1. **Taiwan**
   Date: _____
   Capital: _____
   PCI 1998: _____

2. **South Korea**
   Date: _____
   Capital: _____
   PCI 1998: _____

3. **Cambodia**
   Date: _____
   Capital: _____
   PCI 1998: _____

4. **Philippines**
   Date: _____
   Capital: _____
   PCI 1998: _____

5. **Japan**
   Date: _____
   Capital: _____
   PCI 1998: _____

6. **Hong Kong**
   Date: _____
   PCI 1998: _____

7. **North Korea**
   Date: _____
   Capital: _____
   PCI 1998: _____

8. **Laos**
   Date: _____
   Capital: _____
   PCI 1998: _____

9. **Myanmar (Burma)**
   Date: _____
   Capital: _____
   PCI 1998: _____

10. **China**
    Date: _____
    Capital: _____
    PCI 1998: _____

11. **Singapore**
    Date: _____
    Capital: _____
    PCI 1998: _____

12. **Vietnam**
    Date: _____
    Capital: _____
    PCI 1998: _____

13. **Thailand**
    Date: _____
    Capital: _____
    PCI 1998: _____

14. **Indonesia**
    Date: _____
    Capital: _____
    PCI 1998: _____

15. **Malaysia**
    Date: _____
    Capital: _____
    PCI 1998: _____

Extra Challenge: Use the per capita income figures to construct a bar graph that shows visually the discrepancies in income among the nations of this region.

Nationalist Leaders of Asia and Africa

Directions: Match each nationalist leader listed on the right with the correct description on the left. Write the letter of the leader on the line next to the description.

_____ 1. South Africa's first black president; he had previously been jailed for 27 years for sabotage and treason.

_____ 2. Indonesia's nationalist leader and first president, ruling from 1945 to 1968

_____ 3. Leader of the Muslim League in India and founding father of Pakistan

_____ 4. Ghana's independence leader, served as Ghana's president-for-life while pursuing a Pan-African policy

_____ 5. Nguyen Tat Thanh, Vietnam's nationalist leader who adopted a name meaning "the Enlightener"

_____ 6. Poet-president of Senghor, held office for 20 years

_____ 7. First president of Tanzania, he promoted *ujamaa*, "familyhood," a form of rural socialism.

_____ 8. Nationalist leader of Algeria, later placed under house arrest

_____ 9. First prime minister of Congo, assassinated the next year

_____ 10. Won agreement for Burma's independence but was assassinated before independence day occurred

_____ 11. Longtime head of China's Communist party and the prime leader of the Chinese Revolution

_____ 12. Indian leader known to his followers by a name that means "Great Soul"

a. Mahatma Ghandhi

b. Muhammad Ali Jinnah

c. Léopold Senghor

d. Ahmed Ben Bella

e. Nelson Mandela

f. Aung San

g. Mao Zedong

h. Julius Nyerere

i. Kwame Nkrumah

j. Sukarno

k. Patrice Lumumba

l. Ho Chi Minh

Extra Challenge: Write a biography of any one of these nationalist leaders.

The Modern Global World

The objective of this unit is to help students better understand elements of the modern global world, including global links and joint actions, sources of tension and conflict, advances in science and technology, the nature of the modern global economy, and today's patterns of life. The threat of nuclear war, the global economy, and regional conflicts drew the world's nations into increasing cooperation in the latter half of the twentieth century. That cooperation continues today. The end of the Cold War seemed to promise a lessening of worldwide conflict, but regional conflicts emerged as a new threat. Terrorism has replaced Cold War threats as a global concern in recent times. Advances in science and technology have had a major impact on life, but those advances have had some negative impacts, actual and potential. Similarly, the global economy has overtaken the world, with both positive and negative impacts. Patterns of life have also been affected, with urban and world populations growing rapidly and also migrating, and a global culture creating both unity and forces for disunity. The activities of this unit are designed to draw students into a better understanding of these elements of today's global world.

Student Activities

Worksheet 1, Science and Technology, has students identify the benefits and disadvantages of important advances in science and technology—the computer, genetic engineering, cloning, industrial technology, and the Green Revolution.

Worksheet 2, Adventures in Space, has students trace milestones of the U.S.-Soviet space race, which brought contact between Earth and many other bodies in our solar system.

Worksheet 3, U.N. Peacekeeping, uses mapping to familiarize students with the global reach of U.N. peacekeeping activities over the decades. On the worksheet, students give the date of each listed U.N. mission and a brief description of the conflict it involved.

Worksheet 4, World Trade Blocs, demonstrates the pervasiveness of trading blocs around the world and the number of nations that belong to one or more of them by having students list the nations that belong to each of 13 blocs named on the worksheet. The Extra Challenge underscores the pervasiveness by having students show each of these trading blocs on their map of the world.

Worksheet 5, World Population Growth, presents pie charts that show patterns of world population growth. Students analyze the information in the charts by answering a series of questions. The Extra Challenge invites students to use the information about billion-population markers to create a line graph of world population growth.

Worksheet 6, Urban Growth, presents world and urban population figures over 25-year spans from 1950 through 2025. Students calculate percentages of growth, identify a pattern of growth, and describe social, economic, and environmental effects of this growth. The Extra Challenge invites students to imagine themselves as a young person from a rural village in a less developed nation who moves to a modern city, and to describe the changes this person experiences.

Worksheet 7, The World's Environment, has students explain the causes and effects of the widespread environmental problems of pollution, species extinction, deforestation, erosion and desertification, and garbage accumulation. The Extra Challenge invites students to make an in-depth study of one of these problems and develop a well-reasoned plan to address it.

Worksheet 8 , The Earth's Future: Two Views, presents two very different views of the future of the earth's environment from a 1992 debate at Columbia University. Students choose one side of this issue, investigate further, gather statistics, prepare a position, and engage in a class discussion/debate.

Worksheet 9, Viewpoints: The Muslim Middle East, the United States, and Terrorism, presents viewpoints widely held "on the street" in the Muslim Middle East, which have varying degrees of validity according to one's point of view. Students act as impartial panelists and respond to each expression.

The Modern Global World

Global Links and Actions

In the decades since World War II ended, the threat of nuclear war has hovered over the world. In response, nations have banded together in large and small groups to keep peace and defuse conflicts.

The United Nations was established in 1945 as a public forum for resolving disputes among nations. Representatives from 189 nations debate issues in the U.N.'s General Assembly. U.N. agencies provide social services to millions of people. The United Nations also provides lightly armed soldiers to keep peace between clashing parties. U.N. soldiers from many different nations have been deployed around the globe multiple times.

United Nations building, New York

Nations have also banded together in various military alliances and numerous trading **blocs.** Many international organizations supplement the work of the U.N. agencies around the world. For example, the World Bank provides loans to developing nations. The International Red Cross helps victims of natural disasters and armed conflicts.

> One of the largest and best-known military alliances is NATO, the North Atlantic Treaty Organization. It includes the United States and most nations of Europe. NATO was formed as a defense against communism in 1949. It now includes formerly communist nations of eastern Europe.

To meet the nuclear threat, nations wrote and signed treaties to limit the arms race. Nations that signed the Nuclear Non-Proliferation Treaty of 1968 pledged to halt the proliferation, or spread, of nuclear weapons. The United States and the Soviet Union signed a series of agreements from the 1970s through the 1990s to limit nuclear arms.

The threat of a worldwide nuclear war faded as the Cold War ended. But new threats came to the forefront. Regional conflicts loomed large. Racial and ethnic tensions exploded into violence in many areas. **Fundamentalist** religious rulers imposed strict Muslim law on nations such as Iran and Afghanistan. They have inspired radical Muslims to clash with secular governments in other countries. Rival nations India and Pakistan threaten to use nuclear weapons against one another. Smaller nations such as Iraq and North Korea have tried to develop their own nuclear weapons for possible use against perceived enemies.

(continued)

The Modern Global World *(continued)*

> Examples of racial and ethnic violence in the 1990s include
>
> - mutual slaughter of Hutus and Tutsis in Rwanda
> - "ethnic cleansing" and other killings among Serbs, Croats, and Bosnians in the former Yugoslavia
> - mutual murder of Protestants and Catholics in Northern Ireland

Perhaps the greatest danger to collective security in recent times is the rise of terrorism. Terrorists use random acts of violence against civilians to make a political point, take revenge, and affect government policies. In some cases, nations are believed to sponsor terrorists—training and arming them to carry out operations in other countries. Libya, for example, has been held responsible for the planting of a bomb that blew up a commercial airliner over Scotland in 1988. After Middle Eastern terrorists flew jetliners into buildings in the United States in 2001, U.S. President Bush declared a worldwide "war on terror."

> The most devastating act of terrorism in America occurred on September 11, 2001. Terrorists belonging to the Middle Eastern al-Qaida network flew passenger jetliners into the World Trade Center towers in New York City and into the Pentagon, near Washington, D.C. Passengers brought down another hijacked plane in rural Pennsylvania. Altogether, nearly 3,000 people were killed.

Science and Technology

Advances in science and technology have had a major impact on life in the later twentieth century. These impacts continue in the early twenty-first century:

- Programs to send capsules into space brought new knowledge about our solar system. They also put global communications satellites into orbit.
- Tiny silicon chips were developed for space programs. They made small personal computers possible.
- The **Internet** created a global network of computers. In the 1990s, millions of businesses and individuals became linked through the Internet.
- Medical advances greatly improved health care. New devices—such as CAT scans and ultrasound—allowed improved surgery and better diagnosis. Organ transplants became common.
- Genetic engineering and cloning emerged. They promised new treatments of disease and enhanced plant types.
- The "Green Revolution" developed new strains that increased yields of food crops.

These advances did have some potential downsides, however. For example, genetic changes might spread into unintended areas. The new Green Revolution crops require increased use of chemicals.

(continued)

The Modern Global World (continued)

The Global Economy

Nations have been linked by trade for many centuries. Today, world trade dominates the globe. Huge cargo ships filled with containers carry goods around the world at reasonable cost. Computers process currency transfers from one country to another instantly. Giant multinational corporations conduct their operations in many different countries. They may produce goods in one country and ship them to another for assembly.

To enhance world trade, many nations have promoted **free trade.** They have lowered **tariffs** over the years. Nations within regions have banded together in trading blocs. Within these blocs, few barriers to trade exist.

> Important trade blocs include
> - OPEC, the Organization of Petroleum Exporting Countries, which affects oil prices.
> - The European Union, which has set up standard trade rules and a single currency for the nations of Europe.

However, the global economy is not balanced. A great disparity exists between **developed nations** and **developing nations.** The developed nations are mostly in the global north. The developing nations are mostly in the global south. (The thriving economies of Asia's Pacific Rim are an exception to this north-south pattern.) The developed nations control most of the world's capital and trade. The developing nations are home to manufacturing plants that can pay eager workers low wages. While world trade links rich and poor nations, the economic gap between them increases.

The expanding global economy has had a great impact on the earth's environment. For example:

- The world's oil resources are consumed at an enormous rate.
- Mining destroys land, while cash-crop plantations destroy forests.
- Chemicals used to boost crop production pollute land and water.
- Farming and manufacturing gobble up water resources.
- Gases from factories and energy plants pollute the air.

Patterns of Life

The world has become more urban and less rural. Jobs in industry continue to replace farming activities. As people migrate to the cities for jobs, urban areas grow. Many rural migrants live in dreadful slum conditions in the cities. Yet others find jobs and a degree of escape from poverty. World population continues to grow, so pressures on both rural and urban resources also grow.

Urban life and the spread of world trade have boosted the growth of a more global culture. Mass media have blanketed the world with Western culture. As a result, Western fashions and material goods have become a part of the cultures of many non-Western nations. In return, Western culture has become more international. But the powerful impact of Western values has sparked anti-Western reaction.

Migration has been a hallmark of modern life. People flow from nation to nation. They are spurred by war, ethnic conflict, famine, and a need for jobs.

Science and Technology

Directions: Science and technology have made big advances since 1950, with great impact on people's lives. These advances have brought many benefits, but also some disadvantages. Explain the possible benefits and disadvantages of the advances named below.

1. Widespread computer use
   Benefits: _____
   _____

   Disadvantages: _____
   _____

2. Genetic engineering
   Benefits: _____
   _____

   Disadvantages: _____
   _____

3. Cloning
   Benefits: _____
   _____

   Disadvantages: _____
   _____

4. Technology replacing human workers in industry
   Benefits: _____
   _____

   Disadvantages: _____
   _____
   _____

5. Green Revolution
   Benefits: _____
   _____

   Disadvantages: _____
   _____

Adventures in Space

Directions: The "space race" between the United States and the Soviet Union spurred many remarkable contacts within our solar system. Give the date and spacecraft name for each orbiting, flyby, and landing noted below.

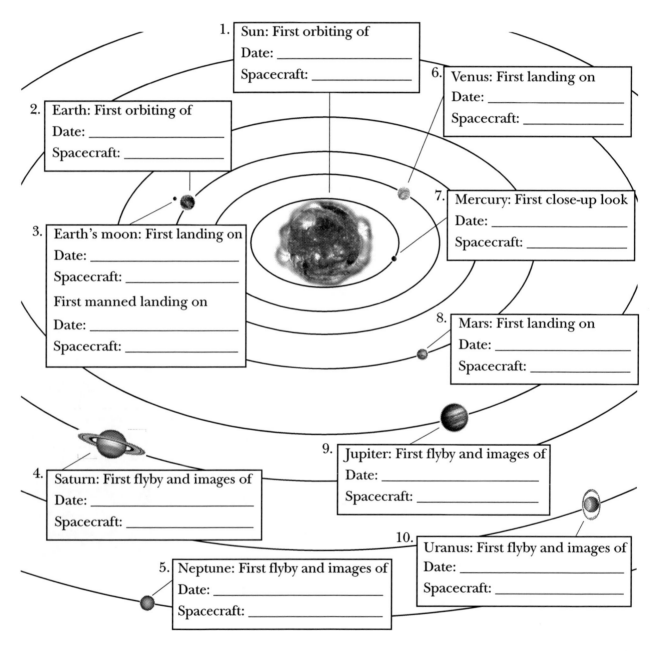

1. Sun: First orbiting of
   Date: _____
   Spacecraft: _____

2. Earth: First orbiting of
   Date: _____
   Spacecraft: _____

3. Earth's moon: First landing on
   Date: _____
   Spacecraft: _____
   First manned landing on
   Date: _____
   Spacecraft: _____

4. Saturn: First flyby and images of
   Date: _____
   Spacecraft: _____

5. Neptune: First flyby and images of
   Date: _____
   Spacecraft: _____

6. Venus: First landing on
   Date: _____
   Spacecraft: _____

7. Mercury: First close-up look
   Date: _____
   Spacecraft: _____

8. Mars: First landing on
   Date: _____
   Spacecraft: _____

9. Jupiter: First flyby and images of
   Date: _____
   Spacecraft: _____

10. Uranus: First flyby and images of
    Date: _____
    Spacecraft: _____

U.N. Peacekeeping

Directions: The United Nations has acted as a peacekeeper many times, all over the globe. Locate and label each of these peacekeeping operations on your map of the world, along with the date each began. Briefly explain below what conflict the United Nations was trying to defuse.

1. India-Pakistan

   Date: _____

   Conflict: _____

   _____

2. East Timor

   Date: _____

   Conflict: _____

   _____

3. Rwanda

   Date: _____

   Conflict: _____

   _____

4. Iraq/Kuwait

   Date: _____

   Conflict: _____

   _____

5. Iran/Iraq

   Date: _____

   Conflict: _____

   _____

6. Cyprus

   Date: _____

   Conflict: _____

   _____

7. Dominican Republic

   Date: _____

   Conflict: _____

   _____

8. Cambodia

   Date: _____

   Conflict: _____

   _____

9. Sierra Leone

   Date: _____

   Conflict: _____

   _____

10. Somalia

    Date: _____

    Conflict: _____

    _____

11. Lebanon

    Date: _____

    Conflict: _____

    _____

12. Bosnia and Herzegovina

    Date: _____

    Conflict: _____

    _____

13. Guatemala

    Date: _____

    Conflict: _____

    _____

14. Haiti

    Date: _____

    Conflict: _____

    _____

World Trade Blocs

Directions: Nations around the world have united in many regional trade blocs. They promote free trade within each bloc. Identify each nation that belongs to each of the trading blocs named here.

 1. Andean Community of Nations:

 2. Asia-Pacific Economic Cooperation (APEC):

 3. Association of South East Asian Nations (ASEAN):

 4. Caribbean Community and Common Market (CARICOM):

 5. Common Market for Eastern and Southern Africa (COMESA):

 6. The Commonwealth of Independent States (CIS):

 7. Council of Arab Economic Unity:

 8. Economic Community of West African States (ECOWAS):

 9. The European Union (EU):

10. North American Free Trade Agreement (NAFTA):

11. Organization of the Petroleum Exporting Countries (OPEC):

12. Southern African Development Community (SADC):

13. Southern Common Market (Mercosur/Mercosul):

> **Extra Challenge:** Use color-coding to show each of these trading blocs on your map of the world.

World Population Growth

Directions: The charts on this page and the next show patterns of world population growth from January 1, 1998, to December 31, 1998. Use the information in the charts to complete the exercises and answer the questions below the charts on the next page.

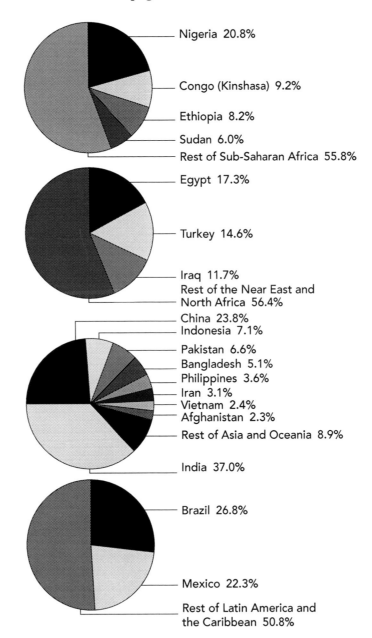

Sub-Saharan Africa

Total population increase in 1998
15.7 million

Percent of total world
population increase
20.0

- Nigeria 20.8%
- Congo (Kinshasa) 9.2%
- Ethiopia 8.2%
- Sudan 6.0%
- Rest of Sub-Saharan Africa 55.8%

Near East and North Africa

Total population increase in 1998
7.1 million

Percent of total world
population increase
9.0

- Egypt 17.3%
- Turkey 14.6%
- Iraq 11.7%
- Rest of the Near East and North Africa 56.4%

Asia and Oceania

Total population increase in 1998
44.7 million

Percent of total world
population increase
56.8

- China 23.8%
- Indonesia 7.1%
- Pakistan 6.6%
- Bangladesh 5.1%
- Philippines 3.6%
- Iran 3.1%
- Vietnam 2.4%
- Afghanistan 2.3%
- Rest of Asia and Oceania 8.9%
- India 37.0%

Latin America and the Caribbean

Total population increase in 1998
7.8 million

Percent of total world
population increase
9.9

- Brazil 26.8%
- Mexico 22.3%
- Rest of Latin America and the Caribbean 50.8%

Source: U.S. Bureau of the Census, *World Population Profile: 1998*

(continued)

World Population Growth *(continued)*

More Developed Countries

Total population increase in 1998
2.9 million

Percent of total world
population increase
3.7

Rest of
MDCs 18.4%

United States 81.6%

**Years taken to reach successive
billion population markers**

2 billion in 1927 123
3 billion in 1960 33
4 billion in 1974 14
5 billion in 1987 13
6 billion in 1999 12
7 billion in 2012* 13
8 billion in 2026* 14
9 billion in 2043* 17

* Projected figures

Source: U.S. Bureau of the Census, *World Population Profile: 1998*

1. Calculate the total numbers of people added to each of the following nations' populations in 1998. Write your answers in the spaces below and next to each country's percentage figure on the pie charts.

   Nigeria _____   Congo _____   Ethiopia _____
   Sudan _____   Egypt _____   Turkey _____
   Iraq _____   China _____   India _____
   Brazil _____   Mexico _____   United States _____

2. What percentage of world population growth occurred in Africa, Asia, and Latin America in 1998? _____

3. Which region gained the most population? _____
   Which region gained the least population? _____
   Which country gained the most population? _____

4. China's rate of population increase for 1998 was 0.9 percent. India's was 1.7 percent. What implications does this have for regional population numbers in Asia? _____
   _____

5. What trends do you see in overall population growth from the billion-population chart at the top right of this page? _____
   _____

Extra Challenge: Use the figures in the billion-population chart above to create a line graph of world population growth from 1927 through 2043 (projected).

Urban Growth

Directions: As world population has grown, more and more people have become city dwellers. Study this chart and complete the exercises that follow to learn more about this process of world urbanization.

Year	World population	Urban population	Percentage of people living in urban areas
1950	2.5 billion	750 million	
1975	4 billion	1.5 billion	
2000	6 billion	3 billion	
2025	8 billion	4.8 billion	

1. Calculate the percentage of total people in the world living in cities for each year on the chart. Write your answers in the blank spaces on the chart.

2. What pattern of urban population growth do you see from the completed chart?

   _____

   _____

3. What effects has the growth in urban populations and urban centers had in the following areas?

   Social: _____

   _____

   _____

   Economic: _____

   _____

   _____

   Environmental: _____

   _____

   _____

Billboard promoting China's "One Family, One Child" policy

Extra Challenge: Imagine you are a young person in a less developed nation. You move with your family from your rural village to a modern city. Write a series of journal entries about the changes, good and bad, in your life and the lives of your family members as you adjust to urban life.

The World's Environment

Directions: The world's economy constantly develops, and this causes great problems for the world's environment. Explain the causes and effects of the widespread environmental problems listed below.

1. Pollution (water, air)

   Causes: _____

   _____

   _____

   Effects: _____

   _____

   _____

2. Species extinction

   Causes: _____

   _____

   Effects: _____

   _____

3. Deforestation

   Causes: _____

   _____

   Effects: _____

   _____

4. Erosion, desertification

   Causes: _____

   _____

   Effects: _____

   _____

5. Garbage accumulation

   Causes: _____

   _____

   Effects: _____

   _____

Extra Challenge: Choose one of these problems, and familiarize yourself with the current global situation. Then develop a well-reasoned, practical plan to manage the problem and reduce its harmful effects on the environment.

The Earth's Future: Two Views

Is the earth's environment doomed? Or can the environment adapt to population and economic growth? New York City's Columbia University sponsored a debate on this issue in October 1992. The debate featured two men with very different views, Julian Simon and Norman Myers. Below is a summary of each man's main arguments.

Position of Julian Simon, American professor and expert on effects of population changes

- U.S. air and water have been getting cleaner for the past 20 years. The U.S. Environmental Protection Agency (EPA) confirms this.
- The prices of natural resources have been falling for decades. This proves that natural resources have been getting more available rather than more scarce.
- The diets of people around the world have continually improved since the mid-twentieth century.
- As world population has constantly increased, so has world economic growth.

Position of Norman Myers, British expert on species extinction and environmental degradation

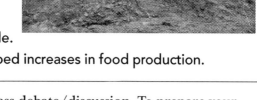

The world's environment is being degraded in a massive way. In the past year
- 25 billion tons of topsoil have eroded.
- 150,000 square kilometers of tropical forests have been destroyed.
- Tens of thousands of species have become extinct.
- More of the ozone layer has disappeared.
- World population has grown by 93 million people.

Since 1985, world population growth has outstripped increases in food production.

Directions: Choose a side on this issue to support in a class debate/discussion. To prepare your position, gather statistics that support your argument and refute the opposition's stand. Develop persuasive points.

Viewpoints: The Muslim Middle East, the United States, and Terrorism

Directions: Below are some perceptions widely held by people in the Muslim Middle East today. They express feelings and opinions that radicals have taken to extremes to fuel and justify anti-American terrorism. As a member of an impartial panel, evaluate and respond to each expression.

1. U.S. foreign policy in the Middle East is directed against the Arab and Muslim world.

2. Action by armed forces—including a nation's military—against unarmed civilians is a form of terrorism. And everyone has the right to fight terrorism.

3. The United States didn't help Arabs or Muslims by sending troops into Kuwait and Saudi Arabia. The Americans were just looking out for their own interests, protecting their oil sources.

4. The presence of U.S. troops on the Arabian peninsula is a sacrilegious infidel occupation of sacred Muslim land.

5. The United States declares its support for human rights and democracy. But it supports corrupt, dictatorial Middle East regimes that oppress their people. The United States has no interest in the common people of the Muslim and Arab world.

6. Israeli military forces kill Palestinians with American weapons. The United States does nothing to stop this. So Palestinians, Arabs, and Muslims everywhere have the right to retaliate against Americans.

7. The U.S. war on terrorism is a war against Muslims, a war against Islam.

8. The United States insists on enforcement of the sanctions against Iraq. Because of this, millions of Iraqis—including millions of children—die of starvation. Why shouldn't American civilians die, too?

9. In countries like Egypt, police and military forces arrest, detain, and then torture and beat dissidents. These police and military get their training in the United States.

10. The United States uses the presence of Saddam Hussein as leader of Iraq as an excuse to keep its troops stationed in the Gulf region. The troops are really there to protect U.S. oil sources.

ANSWERS, ADDITIONAL ACTIVITIES, AND ASSESSMENTS

Note: URLs for listed Internet sites sometimes change. If a given URL does not work, try entering the title of the site into a search engine.

Unit 1. The Twentieth Century Begins

Worksheet 1: New Technologies (page 7)

1. Automobile: late 1800s; pioneers include Karl Benz and Gottlieb Daimler in Germany, Louis Renault in France, Charles and Frank Duryea and Henry Ford in the United States

2. Aircraft: 1903, Wilbur and Orville Wright of the United States

3. Electricity: 1879, 1880s; Thomas Edison of the United States; poles and electric transmission lines become part of the landscape.

4. Telephone: 1876; Alexander Graham Bell of the United States; poles and telephone lines become part of the landscape.

5. Typewriter: 1868; Christopher Latham Sholes of the United States

6. Vacuum cleaner: 1907/08; James Murray Spangler of the United States (it became the Hoover)

Worksheet 2: Industrial vs. Rural Life (page 8)

Typical housing: rural—village cottage or hut; industrial—substantial house or apartment building

Location within the country: rural—countryside; industrial—urban areas

Diet: rural—extremely simple, basic; industrial—varied

Clothing: rural—homemade, often from homemade textiles; industrial—store-bought

Employment: rural—agriculture; industrial—factory, store, business office, with chance to change at will

Health care: rural—mostly folk remedies, herbalists; industrial—doctors, nurses, hospitals, widely available in some form

Leisure time and activities: rural—very little; industrial—evenings and half weekends available for radio, movies, sports, etc.

Travel: rural—almost none, stay in and near home village; industrial—trains and trolleys, to work and beyond

Type of income: rural—mostly produce and barter; industrial—cash

Education: rural—little or none; industrial—public education available, although children stop schooling early in poor families

Family structure: rural—extended family; industrial—nuclear family

Life as a woman: rural—help with family farm and cottage-industry work, care for children and household; industrial—work as stay-at-home mother and wife, or work for pay outside the home

Worksheet 3: Social and Political Ideas (page 9)

Part 1

1. Conservatism (statement is by Konstantin Pobyedonostsev, Russian statesman)

2. Socialism (passage is from the German Social Democratic Party program)

3. Progressivism (passage is from the U.S. Progressive Party platform)

Part 2: Choices and answers will vary.

Worksheet 4: World Trade, World Environments (page 10)

Part 1:

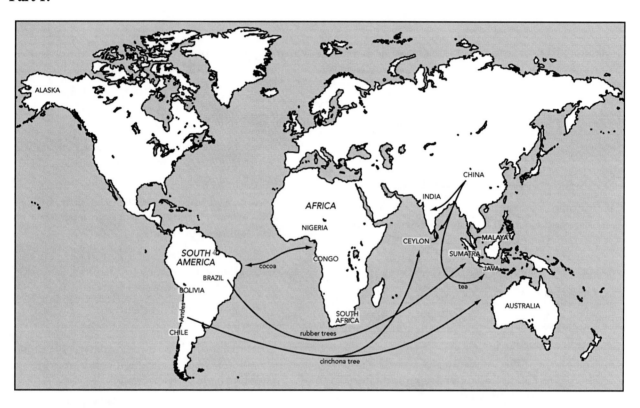

Part 2

1. Mining—creates pollution with slag heaps and poisonous runoff; strip mines create desolate, cratered land.

2. Railroad building—process creates voracious appetites for resources and land; cuts through mountains, bridges rivers and canyons; covers huge amounts of land with freight yards; consumes great amounts of iron, timber, and coal; causes proliferation of people, farms, and urban areas.

3. Cash-crop plantations—transform forests to permanent farms and plantations, replacing shifting slash-and-burn farming practices that allow abandoned farm areas to regenerate;

clear forests, terrace hillsides, drain swamps, consume water resources.

Part 3: Guide students in a class discussion about producing crops for world trade purposes vs. for self-sufficient consumption. Is there any justification for the concept that the lands of a self-sufficient nation are "entirely wasted" by being used to produce crops only for the people who live there?

Worksheet 5: Urban Reforms (page 11)

Students can read the hypertext edition of Jacob Riis's *How the Other Half Lives* on the Internet at www.cis.yale.edu/amstud/inforev/riis/title.html.

Hazardous conditions in tenements: very little light or fresh air inside; hallways and stairwells completely dark; inadequate sewage system (sinks stink); no water during hot summer months; no medical care for sick children; dirty living conditions; blocked fire escapes

Reforms: varied by country; examples—housing codes, fire codes, sanitation codes, and enforcement of them; public health initiatives; improvements in public services, such as water and sewage systems, fire protection, and sanitation; settlement houses and clubs; public parks and other open spaces

Worksheet 6: The Mexican Revolution (page 12)

1. Porfirio Díaz: mestizo, mostly Indian; supported by rich hacienda owners, foreign investors; dictator from 1876 to 1911; forced to resign by revolutionaries, died 1915

2. Francisco Madero: from a rich creole family; supported by revolutionaries, common people; led revolt 1910–11, elected president of Mexico 1911, served until 1913; arrested by Huerta's officers 1913 and murdered

3. Victoriano Huerta: poor Huichol Indian family; supported by the military and conservatives; president of Mexico 1913–14; forced out of office and into exile by revolutionaries in 1914, died in 1916

4. Francisco "Pancho" Villa: poor northern family; supported by peasants; bandit and revolutionary leader from 1910 to 1923; assassinated in 1923

5. Emiliano Zapata: southern Indian tenant farm family; supported by peasants; revolutionary leader from 1911 to 1919; lured by Carranza into a trap and murdered in 1919

6. Venustiano Carranza: wealthy creole landowning family; supported by conservatives, landowners; took political leadership of Mexico in 1914–15, elected president 1917, served until 1920; killed in 1920 while trying to raise a private army

7. Alvaro Obregón: middle-class farm family; supported by reformists, common people; elected president in 1920, served until 1928, brought order and end to revolutionary violence; assassinated by a Catholic fanatic in 1928

Worksheet 7: Revolutionary Art (page 13)

Note: This panel is part of a series of murals that Rivera painted in the chapel at the Universidad Antópoma de Chapingo. Students can view this painting on the Internet at www.diegorivera.com/murals/explotadores.html. Students can also learn about Diego Rivera and view more of his artworks at the rest of the site, "The Virtual Diego Rivera Web Museum" at www.diegorivera.com.

The panel shows a light-skinned mining inspector, a dark-skinned armed guard, and a white (i.e., foreign) mine owner oppressing peasant mine workers. The inspector is searching a mine worker, and the mine owner appears to have just slashed at a worker with his riding crop. The title says that such daily oppression of the workers is creating a revolutionary leader in the person of the mine worker who glares at the guard and mine owner. The panel portrays the widespread exploitation of peasants by the elite landowners and mostly foreign mine owners, a key grievance of the Revolution. The exploitation of poor, landless workers by owners of the means of production is a universal theme of revolutionary movements.

Worksheet 8: Bloody Sunday (page 14)

1. Answers will vary somewhat. Conditions for workers were very poor in Russia at the time. Working conditions were terrible, pay was extremely low, and trade unions were outlawed. Workers lived in dreadful slums and had no political voice. Public protest seemed the only way for workers' grievances to be heard by officials.

2. The petitioners asked for better working conditions, more personal freedom and less official oppression, an elected national legislature, and reform of the corrupt government.

3. Liberals wanted government reforms. Spouses and children of workers supported the workers' requests for change. Revolutionaries preferred more extreme action, but might have joined the march.

4. The tsar's generals and police chiefs ordered the firing; the tsar was not at the palace at the time. They knew that Tsar Nicholas opposed all reform and any defiance of his absolute autocracy. They were no doubt alarmed at being confronted by tens of thousands (possibly hundreds of thousands) of protesters.

5. Discontent exploded across the country, with strikes, terrorism, and peasant and worker revolt. Nicholas was forced to announce reforms in October 1905.

Worksheet 9: Life of Chinese Peasants (page 15)

Part 1

1. Amount of land available is constantly shrinking as the population grows and no new lands are available to open to farming; many peasant farmers become landless farm laborers.

2. Half of your harvest goes to rent and taxes.

3. You eat grains and vegetables.

4. The Hwang He (Yellow River) often floods; in times of chaos, with weak or corrupt government, dikes fall into disrepair.

5. Bandits and armies frequently plunder the countryside.

6. Footbinding restricts your life.

7. Armies plunder and loot; dikes, canals, roads, and bridges fall into disrepair; crops are destroyed; famine kills millions.

Part 2

1. Foreign control of portions of China would end, freeing the land and its resources for use by the peasant population.

2. "People's rights" refers to democracy—you would have a say in choosing government officials and deciding on government policies, which you could influence to be favorable to peasant farming interests.

3. "People's livelihood" refers to economic security for all Chinese, including the exploited peasant class.

Additional Activity Suggestions

You could have students do any of the following additional activities.

1. Create a graph of urban population growth from 1800 to the early 1900s.

2. Write an account of the invention of one of these new technologies of the early twentieth century: the automobile, the telephone, electric power, the radio, the airplane, the phonograph, or motion pictures.

3. Research the life of a leading western conservative, liberal, or socialist who was active in the early part of the twentieth century. Create a biography of your subject that includes a discussion of her or his ideas and impact.

4. Create a poster promoting one of these slogans of the Mexican Revolution: "Liberty, Order, and Progress" (Benito Juárez); "Order and Progress" (Porfirio Díaz); "Land and Liberty!" (Emiliano Zapata).

5. Create a class display of the mural art of Diego Rivera, José Clemente Orozco, and David Alfaro Siqueiros expressing scenes and themes of the Mexican Revolution.

6. Compare the goals and strategies of China's May Fourth Movement with those of Japan's earlier Meiji Restoration.

7. Investigate any of these Internet sites:

   "Bloody Sunday":
   http://www.spartacus.schoolnet.co.uk/
   RUSsunday.htm

   "Don Mabry's Historical Text Archive—Mexican Revolution":
   http://historicaltextarchive.com/
   links.php?op=viewslink&sid=224

   "Father George Gapon":
   http://www.angelfire.com/dc/1spy/
   Gapon.html

   "Lower East Side Tenement Museum":
   http://www.tenement.org/

   "1900 vs. Now—TIMEwarp":
   http://cgi.pathfinder.com/time/time100/
   timewarp/timewarp.html

"Postcards of the Mexican Revolution":
http://www.netdotcom.com/revmexpc/

"Sun Yat Sen":
http://wanqingyuan.zaobao.com/english/
links/links.html

"Technology in 1900":
http://www.pbs.org/wgbh/pages/amex/
kids/tech1900/index.html

Assessment

1. Have students compare the motivations and goals of the supporters of revolution in Mexico, China, and Russia, in chart form.

2. Ask students to identify the changes in the everyday life of an average person in an industrial nation in the early years of the twentieth century.

Unit 2: World War I

Worksheet 1: Causes of the War (page 23)

1. **Nationalism**

   Definition: a feeling, often aggressive, of deep pride in one's country

   How it worked toward war: Aggressive nationalists wanted to expand their nation's power and territory at the expense of other nations.

   Specific examples: Answers will vary; include French desire for revenge on Germany and regaining of Alsace-Lorraine; Pan-Slavism in eastern Europe.

2. **Militarism**

   Definition: glorifying of the military and focusing on being ready for war

   How it worked toward war: National policy was heavily influenced toward going to war against rival nations, and militarism fueled an intense arms race.

   Specific examples: Answers will vary; include German-British naval expansion; growing influence of German generals and British admirals over their nations' foreign policy.

3. **Imperialism**

   Definition: policy of seeking to gain control over other countries

   How it worked toward war: Nations of Europe clashed in regions overseas as they jockeyed for colonies.

   Specific examples: Answers will vary; include France and Germany going to the brink of war over Morocco.

4. **Alliance system**

   Definition: network of agreements among two or more nations that each will come to the aid of one of the others if it is attacked by any other country

   How it worked toward war: Conflict between any two members of opposing alliance groups could draw in all the other members of the alliances.

   Specific examples: Answers will vary; the string of declarations of war after the assassination at Sarajevo demonstrates the effect.

Worksheet 2: Steps to War (page 24)

You could conduct this activity as a class discussion, point by point, or set it up as a small-group activity. Each group could formulate an alternative to one or two steps, or each group could formulate alternatives for one of the six nations involved in this activity.

Worksheet 3: The Tools of War (page 25)

1. Machine gun: fires a rapid, continuous stream of bullets; a few gunners can quickly mow down waves of attackers, making advance across no-man's land extremely difficult.

2. Submarine: ship that operates underwater; it attacks ships with underwater torpedoes, can approach enemy ships underwater unseen and strike without warning; German U-boat attacks crippled Allied shipping and brought the United States into the war.

3. Tank: armored vehicle that moves on chain tracks, so it can traverse many types of terrain; advances on enemy soldiers and fires on them, with soldiers inside the tank protected from enemy fire.

4. Airplane: one- or two-seat open aircraft; first use of the airplane in war—first used to observe enemy positions, then armed with bombs to drop on enemy positions and with machine guns that individual pilots used to engage in "dogfights" with one another.

5. Poison gas: various gases that cause blinding, severe blisters, and/or choking; gas masks were soon developed to protect soldiers.

Worksheet 4: Mapping World War I (page 26)

You might choose to assign selected mapping activities to students.

Part 1: Check mapped locations on any standard map of the world. The Russo-Japanese War was fought in Manchuria and the Sea of Japan. The Italo- Turkish War was fought in the Mediterranean region. The Balkan wars were fought in the Balkan region.

Part 2:

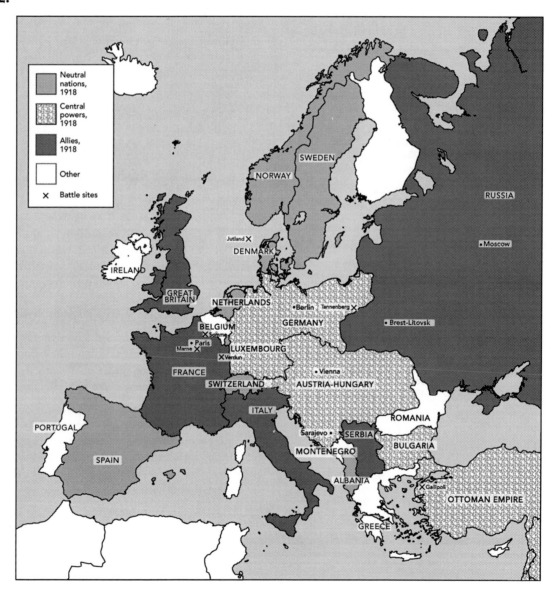

Part 3: Labels should give the following information.

Southwest Asia: Arabs fought Turks here.

East Asia: Japan seized German outposts in China and the Pacific islands.

Africa: Allies fought for German colonies of Togo, Southwest Africa, German Cameroon, and Tanganyika.

India: provided 1.3 million personnel for Allied service

Europe: main theater of the war, with Allies fighting Central Powers, mostly on the western and eastern fronts

Brazil: contributed warships and personnel to Allies

United States: entered the war in 1917 after repeated German attacks on its ships in the Atlantic Ocean

Australia, New Zealand: contributed troops to the Allies, especially for the Battle of Gallipoli

Part 4:

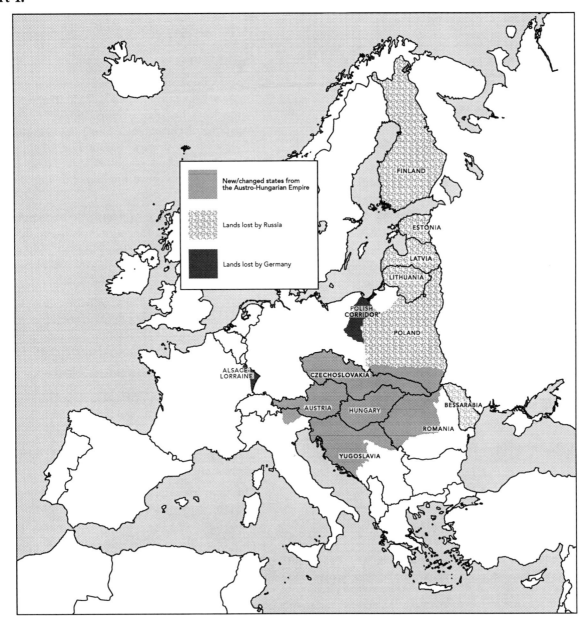

Worksheet 5: Life and Death on the Western Front (page 27)

Interested students could read more or all of Empey's *Over the Top* (Knickerbocker Press, 1917). It's a lively and vivid account of the experiences of trench warfare and life. Students can find more of Wilfred Owen's descriptions, from letters he wrote home from the western front, in the introductory "Memoir" to *The Poems of Wilfred Owen,* Edmund Blunden, editor (The Viking Press, New York, 1931).

Students can find more background for this activity in descriptions of trench warfare conditions in books and web sites about World War I.

As alternative activities, students could create an artwork of trench life or of no-man's land. Or they could perform a skit with classmates, acting the parts of World War I soldiers dealing with life in the trenches and forays into no-man's land.

Worksheet 6: The Appeal of War (page 28)

1. Patriotism: "the Hun" (demonize the enemy), "Hoist the flag," "do your bit" (for your country), "to liberty be true," "the time has come when we must go to war" (to defend our country), "North and South" (all parts of the country)

2. Idealism: "Like true heroes do or die," "Make your mother proud of you," "to liberty be true," "the time has come when we must go to war," "our race was never known to run," "ev'ry mother's son"

3. Excitement: "get your gun, get your gun, get your gun," "true heroes do or die," "show grit," "to the ranks," "You'll be there! You'll be there!" "we're prepared!" "we'll meet them gun to gun"

Worksheet 7: The Horror of War (page 29)

Students can read the entire poem "Dulce et Decorum Est" on the Internet at http://www.emory.edu/ENGLISH/LostPoets/Dulce.html. They can read more World War I poetry at the "Lost Poets" site listed under Additional Activity Suggestion 8.

Answers will vary somewhat. The Cohan and Brennan lyrics are thoroughly patriotic and express an idealistic, exciting image of war, a popular view among patriotic young people who have no previous experience of war. The Owen and Sassoon poems express the dreadful reality and horror of war that initially idealistic young soldiers soon found themselves immersed in.

Worksheet 8: War Propaganda (pages 30–31)

1. Italian poster: (The slogan translates as "Everyone do your duty!"—by subscribing to the latest war loan [*prestito*] program.) War aim: an appeal for Italians to support the national war loan program; Appeal, symbol: visual appeal of the strong, valiant soldier and the direct engagement of the viewer by the finger pointing straight at her/him.

2. U.S. poster: War aim: to encourage the enlistment of able-bodied men to fight in the war; Appeal, symbol, slogan: visual appeal of patriotic father figure (Uncle Sam) using implied flattery via the slogan, "I Want *You*," to appeal to the individual and suggest that *he* is the person the Army needs, pointing finger to engage the viewer.

Challenge Question: Answers will vary; the pointed finger engages viewers individually and also imparts a feeling of responsibility in the viewer about responding to the appeal, techniques that appeal to human emotions across nationalities.

Students' choices and posters for the second page of the activity will vary.

Worksheet 9: War Casualties (page 32)

1. Russia (3.7 million, total)

2. 3.2 million (Germany, Austria-Hungary, Ottoman Empire, Bulgaria)

3. 5.145 million (Portugal, Greece, Montenegro, and Japan also fought with the Allies, with relatively small losses)

4. Ottoman Empire; genocide of Armenians by the Ottoman Turks (accounts for 2 million-plus deaths; the rest were mostly Syrians and Iraqis)

5. United States and Italy; the war was not fought in the United States, and only briefly in northeastern Italy

Worksheet 10:
Objections to the Peace Treaties (page 33)

1. Germany: bitterness and deep anger about the "war guilt" clause and the crushing reparations payments

2. Italy: entered the war to gain territory, angry that it didn't get what it wanted and was promised in a secret treaty with the Allies

3. Japan: entered the war to gain territory, angry that Western nations refused to recognize its claims in China

4. Middle Eastern Arabs: angry that Britain reneged on its promise of Arab independence after the war in return for Arabs helping to fight the Turks in the Middle East

5. China: displeased at having to accept Japanese control over former German colonial holdings in Asia

6. Russia/Soviet Union: angry at being excluded from the peace talks and about reestablishment of Poland and the three independent Baltic states

7. India: deeply resented that service of many Indians in World War I did not result in a rapid movement toward independence, as the British had promised would happen

8. Africa: as in India, deep resentment that service in World War I did not result in independence

Additional Activity Suggestions

You could have students do any of the following additional activities.

1. Read other eyewitness accounts of World War I fighting. One good source is *Eyewitness to History,* edited by John Carey (NY: Avon Books, 1997).

2. Role-play a discussion among German military and political leaders about the pros and cons of reinstating submarine warfare against U.S. supply ships in 1917.

3. Assume the roles of subjects of colonies in Africa and Asia controlled by Great Britain and France. Debate the question of whether or not you should respond positively to your colonial rulers' request that you fight with them in World War I.

4. Research and report on the isolationist movement in the United States and the reasons why the U.S. Senate refused to allow the United States to join the League of Nations.

5. Create a class display of World War I propaganda poster images from a variety of countries. Are the appeals they make similar?

6. Write a nationalist song expressing loyalty to your country and exhorting action in support of a specific cause.

7. Write an essay as an idealist of 1914 explaining why you believe that war in Europe is now a thing of the past, given advances in science, technology, and human reason.

8. Investigate any of these Internet sites:

   "ANZACS Net":
   http://www.anzacs.net/

   "First World War.Com":
   http://www.firstworldwar.com/index.htm

   "The Great War: 80 Years On":
   http://news.bbc.co.uk/1/hi/
   special_report/1998/10/98/world_war_i/
   197437.stm

   "The Great War and the Shaping of the 20th Century":
   http://www.pbs.org/greatwar/

   "Lost Poets of the Great War":
   http://www.emory.edu/ENGLISH/
   LostPoets/index.html

   "World War Web: A World War I History Site":
   http://library.thinkquest.org/12367/

   "World War I: Trenches on the Web" (History Channel):
   http://www.worldwar1.com/

   "The World War I Document Archive":
   http://www.lib.byu.edu/estu/wwi/

Assessment

1. Invite students to participate in a class chorale and poetry reading, contrasting performance of patriotic World War I songs of their choice with readings of antiwar poems by Sassoon, Owen, Rupert Brooke, and others.

2. Ask students to evaluate this statement: "A peace neither of punishment nor of reconciliation, the Treaty of Versailles was one of the greatest failures in history."

Unit 3: The World Between Wars: 1920s and 1930s

Worksheet 1: Different Paths in Europe (page 41)

1. England: democracy; Stanley Baldwin (Conservative) and James Ramsay MacDonald (Labour)

2. France: democracy; constantly revolving governments and leaders

3. Italy: fascist totalitarian state, 1922–1940s; Benito Mussolini

4. Germany: republic 1919–33; Nazi dictatorship 1933–1945; Adolf Hitler

5. Poland: military dictatorship 1926–35; Joseph Pilsudski

6. Czechoslovakia: democracy; Tomáš Masaryk, president 1918–35

7. Hungary: military dictatorship 1919–1944; Miklós Horthy

Answers to Challenge Questions:

1. The countries of western Europe (Britain, France) remained democracies, while the countries of central and eastern Europe turned to dictatorship and totalitarian rule. (Although this is not included as part of the activity, you could point out to students that Yugoslavia, Albania, Bulgaria, and Romania were under strongman rule of kings at this time.)

2. The countries of eastern Europe had no tradition of democracy and could not maintain the democratic governments set up there right after the war; postwar instability in Germany and Italy caused their people to turn to dictators who could impose order.

Worksheet 2: Words of the Times (page 42)

1. c	6. i
2. h	7. a
3. j	8. f
4. b	9. d
5. g	10. e

Worksheet 3: Changes in the Middle East (page 43)

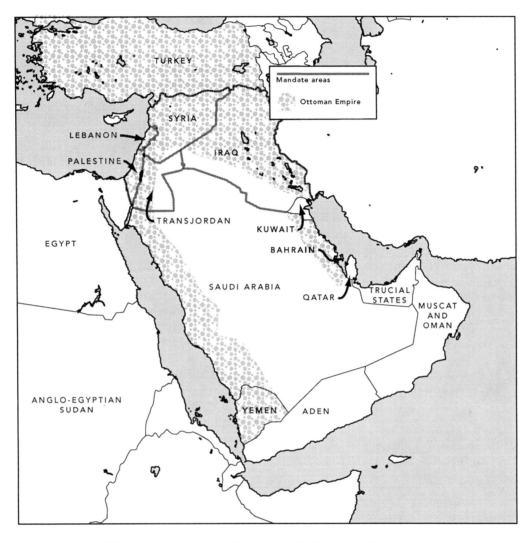

Worksheet 4: Nationalism in Southwest Asia and India (page 44)

1. **Turkey**

   Leader: Kemal Atatürk

   Goals: To modernize Turkey along Western lines

   Changes: Turkey becomes a republic rather than an Islamic state; Islamic law, Islamic calendar, Islamic schools, and Arabic script are replaced with Western versions; people wear Western clothes; women can go out freely in public, vote, and hold public office.

2. **Saudi Arabia**

   Leader: Abd al-Aziz Ibn Saud

   Goals: To unify Arabia under the Saud family

   Changes: Other than unification, few; the Saudi rulers keep to Arab and Islamic traditions and law; some modernization is undertaken, but only as compatible with Islamic culture.

3. **Iran**

   Leader: Reza Shah Pahlavi

   Goals: To modernize the country and free it from British and Russian spheres of influence

   Changes: Like Turkey, Iran becomes a secular rather than an Islamic state, modernized along

Western lines just as in Turkey; Reza Shah keeps all power in his hands.

4. **India**

Leader: Mohandas Gandhi

Goals: Independence from British rule

Changes: Full independence does not come until 1947, but nonviolent protests inspired by Gandhi force Britain to grant India limited self-rule in 1935.

Worksheet 5: Nonviolence: Theory and Practice (page 45)

1. Yes, they were effective. As the marchers walked from village to village, support for Gandhi's movement against British rule spread widely. Embarrassing worldwide publicity about the violence inflicted on peaceful protesters forced the British to make concessions.

2. Many were jailed.

3. Students' responses will vary.

Worksheet 6: Revolution in China (page 46)

Part 1

1. Banker: support Kuomintang—You don't want the socialist economy that the Communists would impose, in which the government would take over banks.

2. Landless peasant: support Communists—The Kuomintang ignores you, while Mao's Communists give you land they have seized from wealthy landlords.

3. Business owner: support Kuomintang—You don't want the socialist economy that the Communists would impose, which would abolish private business.

4. Urban laborer: support Communists—They claim that they will give power to the peasants and the laborers.

5. Landlord: support Kuomintang—The Communists will seize your lands.

6. Warlord: don't support either—Both fight against you to take away your power and local control.

7. Student: might support either one—But many young intellectuals turned against the Western democratic beliefs of the Kuomintang when the West failed to help Sun Yixian's government; also, the Soviet Union offered courses of study to Chinese students who supported the Chinese Communist party.

8. Activist woman: probably would support the Communists, who welcomed women's participation.

9. Military officer: might support either one—Kuomintang might appeal because Jiang Jieshi was an army officer himself; but the Soviet Union would be happy to train you as a potential military vanguard of a communist revolution in China.

Part 2

All along the Long March, Communist soldiers were strictly ordered not to take anything from the peasants without paying for it, and to treat all peasants nicely, and to avoid damaging their crops. This treatment "sowed many seeds" of support among the peasants in all the provinces that the retreating Communists marched through, and when the Communists and the Kuomintang once again fought each other after World War II ended, these "seeds" of support yielded a "crop" of ardent peasant supporters for the Communist side.

Worksheet 7: Marxism: Theory and Practice (page 47)

1. Lenin: An elite group will lead the revolution, setting up a "dictatorship of the proletariat"; the elite will lead because Russia did not have much of an urban proletariat; great change from Marxist theory in that Communist revolution in Russia occurs in a mostly rural country.

2. Stalin acts on the policy of "socialism in one country" rather than the Marxist theory/prediction of worldwide Communist revolution.

3. Mao bases the Chinese Communist revolution on the peasants rather than the proletariat, a radical departure from Marxist theory.

Worksheet 8: "The Crisis of the Spirit" (page 48)

Examples will vary.

1. Examples of Expressionist, Cubist, Dada, or Surrealist artworks would be appropriate.

2. Music with dissonance, irregular rhythm, and harsh sound combinations would be appropriate—e.g., Igor Stravinsky's *The Rite of Spring*, or Arnold Schoenberg's works.

3. Examples could be the war poets (Sassoon, Owen, Brooke), T. S. Eliot's *The Waste Land*, or W. B. Yeats's "The Second Coming."

4. Examples include the writings of Franz Kafka and James Joyce, Ernest Hemingway's *The Sun Also Rises*, F. Scott Fitzgerald's *The Great Gatsby*, and Erich Maria Remarque's *All Quiet on the Western Front*.

Worksheet 9: Women's Lives (page 49)

1. You have access to public education and a wide range of jobs, including advanced-education and -training jobs, such as medicine and engineering; you have access to state-run day-care for your children, which you probably have, because motherhood is a patriotic duty; but you are also responsible for child care and housework at home in your non-wage-earning time.

2. You can go out in public alone, without wearing a veil; you can work outside the home; polygamy is no longer allowed, so you are your husband's only wife; you can vote and hold public office; you have access to free public education.

3. If you are a member of a poor peasant family, you will get land redistributed to you from lands taken from local large landowners.

4. You are valued as a wife and mother, but not as a worker; if you formerly held a job, the fascist regime will replace you with a man.

5. You experience little change; you are still subordinate to men in virtually all things.

6. You might join the self-sufficiency movement, learning to spin and weave your own cloth, and join in nonviolent demonstrations; you are attracted by Gandhi's call for equal rights for all, including women.

7. You can vote, go to college, and pursue many more career options. If you are middle-class or upper-class, you might become a "flapper" and take on all sorts of freedoms, such as bobbed hair, short skirts, unchaperoned dates, and drinking and smoking in public. If you are a housewife, you lose your wartime job, but gain labor-saving home appliances that give you leisure time for volunteerism and other pursuits.

8. You can go out in public without a veil, and you can get a free public education.

9. If "Aryan," you are valued as a mother or potential mother, a producer of more members of the "master race"; you are dismissed from upper-level jobs and denied entry to universities; you suffer severe persecution if you are a Jew or Gypsy.

Worksheet 10: Time Line of the Russian Revolution (page 50)

1905 Revolution and events leading up to it:

early 1900s	Lenin goes into exile in Europe.
1903	Russian Marxists split into two factions: Mensheviks and Bolsheviks.
1904	Trans-Siberian railroad completed.
1904	Russo-Japanese War
1905	Bloody Sunday

Events Between Revolutions:

1906	First Duma meets.
1914	Russia enters World War I.
1915	Tsar Nicholas goes to war front to rally troops.
1916	Rasputin is murdered.

March 1917 Revolution and following events:

March 1917	Petrograd strike and riots
March 1917	Tsar Nicholas abdicates.
March 1917	Kerensky establishes provisional government.
April 1917	Lenin returns to Russia.

November 1917 Revolution and following events:

Nov. 1917	Bolshevik Revolution

1918	Tsar Nicholas and family executed
1918	Treaty of Brest-Litovsk takes Russia out of World War I.
1918–20	Civil war in Russia
1921	New Economic Policy launches.
1922	Russian empire renamed U.S.S.R.
1924	Lenin dies.
1928	Stalin launches first Five-Year Plan.

Worksheet 11: The Soviet Economy (page 51)

Shared elements: state control of financial institutions, foreign trade, large industries, communications, natural resources

NEP only: Small businesses can operate for profit, peasants can own small plots and sell surplus crops, foreign investment is accepted.

Five-Year Plans only: no free markets, no private businesses, no foreign investment; collective farms (all agricultural lands and crops belong to the government); production quotas for all segments of the economy

Worksheet 12: Communism, Fascism, Democracy (page 52)

Ideology: C—dictatorship of proletariat, state over individual; F—authoritarianism, state over individual; D—rule of majority, democracy, representative government

Leaders/leadership: C—supreme authoritarian leader; F—supreme authoritarian leader; D—popularly elected leader

Political party/parties: C—one; F—one; D—multiple

Valued social classes: C—workers and peasants and party bureaucrats; F—middle class, industrialists, military; D—all

Economic policy: C—collective ownership, central state planning; F—private property controlled by the state; D—free-market with some state guidelines or control

State vs. individual rights: C—state over individual; F—state over individual; D—individual over state

Foreign policy: C—spread communism worldwide; F—expansionist; D—varies

Role of police: C—keep populace under strict control as directed by Communist party leadership; F—keep populace under strict control as directed by Fascist leader; D—operate under the rule of law, overseen by judiciary

Worksheet 13: Mass Culture (page 53)

Woman golfer—Life for women in Western countries became much less restrictive. Women wore looser, less restrictive clothing and participated in many activities outside the home, including recreational sports such as golfing. Also, many millions of people—men and women—now had enough leisure time to engage in recreational and spectator sports.

Radio—Americans and Europeans by the millions embraced the home radio during the 1920s, eagerly listening to all kinds of shows, including news, drama, comedy, music, and sports events, that reached entire nations.

Garbage disposal—Most average families eagerly purchased consumer goods, promoted by ubiquitous advertising, and many devices became available to cut down on the toil of housework. The consumer culture and mass marketing became fully entrenched in the Western world during these decades.

Worksheet 14: The Great Depression (page 54)

Part 1

1. Germany borrowed money from New York banks to make the reparations payments required by the Versailles Treaty.

2. Germany sent the borrowed money to France and Britain as war reparation payments.

3. France and Britain used the reparations money to pay back money they had borrowed from the United States to finance the war.

4. U.S. banks could not continue to loan money to Germany, so Germany could not make reparations payments to France and Britain, so they could not pay back the U.S. war loans.

Part 2

Prices of manufactured goods rise to cover higher wage costs.

Consumers can't afford to buy as many higher-priced goods.

Store owners order fewer goods to sell.

Factories produce fewer goods and therefore lay off workers.

Workers who are unemployed can't buy manufactured goods.

Factories cut back more, so lay off more workers.

Workers, more of whom are unemployed, buy even fewer goods, and so the downward spiral continues.

Worksheet 15: Scenes of the Great Depression (page 55)

Student interpretations of the images will vary.

Worksheet 16: Latin America and the United States (page 56)

Check to be sure students have correctly identified the named countries on their maps. You could also have students create a companion map and information key for U.S. involvement in Central America and the Caribbean from the 1960s through the 1990s.

1. Cuba: 1898–1902, 1906–09, 1912; U.S. troop occupation; to guide Cuba to independence after the Spanish-American War (1898–1902), then to restore order

2. Dominican Republic: 1904–05, 1916–24; U.S. troops, customs takeover; to keep order during period of chaos, protecting U.S. business interests

3. Guatemala: 1920; U.S. troops; to keep order when the dictator Cabrera's rule ended

4. Haiti: 1915–34; U.S. troops, financial takeover; to maintain order

5. Honduras: 1919; U.S. troops; to keep order

6. Mexico: 1914, 1916–17; U.S. troops; mainly pursuit of Pancho Villa

7. Nicaragua: 1910–33; U.S. troops, customs takeover; to support conservative pro-business governments

8. Panama: 1903; U.S. warships allow revolution; to create Canal Zone for proposed Panama Canal

9. Puerto Rico: 1898–1900; U.S. troops; to guide transition from Spanish colony after Spanish-American War (inhabitants granted U.S. citizenship, 1917)

10. Virgin Islands: 1917; purchased from Denmark

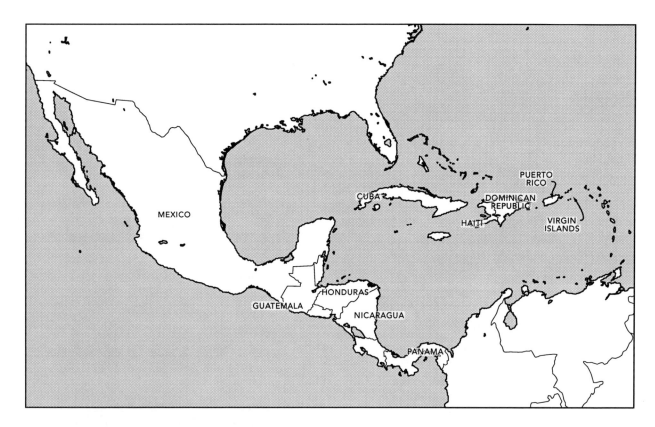

Additional Activity Suggestions

You could have students do any of the following additional activities.

1. Research and report on the environmental impact of the new, widespread popularity of the automobile in the 1920s and 1930s.

2. Create a classroom display of reproductions of 1920s and 1930s art, including examples of Expressionist, Surrealist, Dada, and Cubist styles.

3. On a map of China, trace the "Long March" of the Chinese Communists, showing the daunting geographic obstacles they had to overcome. Or map the fighting among the Communists, the Kuomintang, and the Japanese invaders.

4. Create a chart showing the many international organizations and agreements of the 1920s and 1930s that worked to further peace.

5. Research and report on the League of Nations. Explain its goals and the tools it had, and did not have, to achieve those goals. Also explain which nations joined the League, which did not, and why.

6. Develop a case study of one Latin American nation in the first four decades of the twentieth century, with a focus on its relations with the United States during that time.

7. Chart the major medical advances made between 1900 and 1914, explaining the impact of each one on public health.

8. Investigate any of these Internet sites:

   "America from the Great Depression to World War II: Photographs from the FSA-OWI, 1935–1945":
   http://lcweb2.loc.gov/ammem/fsowhome.html

   "Chronology of Russian History":
   http://www.departments.bucknell.edu/russian/chrono3.html

   "Documents of the Interwar Period":
   http://www.mtholyoke.edu/acad/intrel/interwar.htm

"Mahatma Gandhi Foundation":
  http://www.mahatma.org.in/flash.html

"Marxists.org Internet Archive":
  http://www.marxists.org/index.htm

"Mustafa Kemal Atatürk":
  http://www.ataturk.com/

"The Russian Revolution":
  http://www.barnsdle.demon.co.uk/russ/
  rusrev.html

"Weimar Republic":
  http://www.barnsdle.demon.co.uk/hist/
  weilin.html

Assessment

1. Ask students to create a time line of nationalist and revolutionary movements around the world during the 1920s and 1930s.

2. Have students create a chart that compares specific aspects of the rules of Stalin, Hitler, and Mussolini.

3. Have students trace the ways in which the harsh provisions of the Versailles Treaty that ended World War I worked through the 1920s and 1930s to build toward World War II.

Unit 4. World War II

Worksheet 1: Steps Toward War (page 64)

You could have students trace each of these steps on their map of the world.

1. September 1931, Manchuria: League condemns the aggression (Japan quits League); Western nations protest but do not act.

2. March 1935, German rearmament: League issues a mild condemnation; Western nations do not try to stop this, but simply keep on arming themselves.

3. October 1935, Ethiopia: League condemns attack, votes sanctions that are not enforced; Western nations do nothing—Britain even allows Italian troops and supplies to use the Suez Canal on their way to Ethiopia.

4. March 1936, Rhineland: Western nations do not challenge the aggression.

5. July 1937, China: Western nations protest, do not act.

6. March 1938, Austria: Britain and France ignore their promise to protect Austrian independence.

7. September 1938, Sudetenland: Britain and France agree at Munich Conference to allow the seizure before it happens, and they convince the Czech government to yield without a fight.

8. March 1939, Czechoslovakia: Britain and France are alarmed, promise to protect Poland.

9. April 1939, Albania: Western nations take no action.

10. September 1939, Poland: France and Britain declare war on Germany in response.

Worksheet 2:
The Munich Agreement (page 65)

As you study events of the second half of the twentieth century in Units 5 and 6, call students' attention to ways in which, during the decades after World War II, nations applied the lesson that appeasement does not work.

1. People in Britain and France were repelled by the thought of another European war so soon after the horrors of World War I, the "war to end all wars." Both Britain and France were focused on the economic problems caused by the Great Depression. France was deeply divided politically and needed strong British support to stand up to Hitler, support that was not forthcoming. Many British people thought that Germany had a right to ignore provisions of the Versailles Treaty, because the treaty had been too harsh. Both France and Britain saw a strong Germany as a valuable buffer against the spread of communism from the Soviet Union to the east.

2. Students' alternative responses will vary.

Worksheet 3: War Technology (page 66)

1. Radar: radio device or system for locating an object by reflecting ultra-high-frequency radio waves back from the object (*ra*dio *d*etecting *a*nd *r*anging); used to detect incoming airplanes

2. Aircraft carrier: huge ship that carried fighter planes and bombers; used to fight naval battles of the war in the Pacific

3. Atomic bomb: devastatingly powerful, newly developed bomb that used atomic fission; one dropped on Hiroshima and another on Nagasaki brought the Japanese government to surrender.

4. Sonar: device that detects the presence and location of a submerged object by using sonic and supersonic waves reflected back from the object (*so*und *na*vigation *r*anging); used to locate submerged submarines

Worksheet 4: National Expansion: Two Reactions (page 67)

1. The German Sudeten woman is saluting German Nazi troops marching in to annex the Sudetenland to Germany. She is crying with happiness to have her German-speaking section of Czechoslovakia become part of Germany proper.

2. The French man is crying in sorrow as victorious Nazi troops march into Paris, signaling the fall of France to her long-time enemy Germany.

Worksheet 5: Women War Workers (page 68)

An excellent source for first-person accounts about women's roles in World War II is *The Homefront: America During World War II* by Mark Jonathan Harris et al. (New York: G. P. Putnam's Sons, 1984).

1. The "We Can Do It" woman is famously known as Rosie the Riveter. Her strong, determined facial features and her muscular working arm present a powerful image of woman as strong, capable, responsible, reliable, and hardworking.

2. The Army Nurse Corps woman wears a military uniform and looks cool, efficient, capable, professional, and able to give significant aid to the war effort as a member of the U.S. military.

Worksheet 6: The Holocaust: Why Obey? (page 69)

1. Höss took these actions because he had been ordered to do so by Himmler, acting to carry out Hitler's orders. Responses about justification will vary.

2. Fisch suggests that the following bear some responsibility: other nations who would not ransom Jews, Europeans who helped with the train transportation of people to the concentration camps, and U.S. President Franklin Roosevelt and all others who knew about the mass extermination but did not speak out or act.

3. Responses will vary.

4. Responses will vary.

Worksheet 7: The Atomic Bomb (pages 70–71)

You could suggest that students read first-person accounts by survivors of the atomic bombings of Hiroshima and Nagasaki. Students could then consider the devastating effect of the bombing on Japanese civilians in their role-play debate.

Worksheet 8: War Casualties—World War II (page 72)

1. Soviet Union

2. 4,430,000

3. 8,400,000

4. Soviet Union; millions died in the German invasion, and millions more of disease, starvation, and cold.

5. China; the war against the invading Japanese was lengthy and deadly, and millions of peasants died of famine.

6. United States; the war was not fought on U.S. soil, so few civilians were affected.

Additional Activity Suggestions

You could have students do any of the following additional activities.

1. Research and report on the Spanish civil war, focusing on elements that were precursors of World War II.

2. Create a class display of images of World War II propaganda posters from various countries. What similarities do you see among them? How do these posters compare with ones from World War I?

3. Bombings of civilians became a standard tactic during World War II, by both sides. Compile casualty figures for bombing campaigns against cities such as London, Dresden, and Tokyo. Read eyewitness accounts. Explain why civilian bombing became "acceptable" for combatants during this war. Has targeting of civilians continued as a common tactic of warfare?

4. Trace the course of World War II on a map of the Pacific area, noting significant battles and advances.

5. Research and report on the history of anti-Semitism in Europe over the centuries. Or develop an annotated time line of the history of the Nazis' "war on Jews."

6. Describe the environmental effects of the war in an illustrated report.

7. Investigate any of these Internet sites:

   "America @ War!":
     http://library.thinkquest.org/17573/

   "America from the Great Depression to World War II: Photographs from the FSA-OWI, 1935–1945":
     http://lcweb2.loc.gov/ammem/fsowhome.html

   "Hiroshima/Enola Gay":
     http://ourworld.compuserve.com/homepages/Enola_Gay/links.htm#Hiroshima

   "The History Place: World War Two in Europe":
     http://www.historyplace.com/worldwar2/timeline/ww2time.htm

   "The Holocaust: A Tragic Legacy":
     http://library.thinkquest.org/12663/

   "The Pacific War":
     http://library.thinkquest.org/18106/

   "Remember.org" (Holocaust):
     http://remember.org/

   "The Rutgers Oral History Archives of World War II":
     http://fas-history.rutgers.edu/oralhistory/orlhom.htm

   "World War II":
     http://www.bbc.co.uk/history/war/wwtwo/index.shtml

   "Yahoo! Picture Gallery—World War II":
     http://search.gallery.yahoo.com/search/corbis?p=world+war+ii

Assessment

1. Have students describe the similarities and differences between World War I and World War II, in chart or narrative form.

2. Have students role-play a postwar trial charging U.S. military and political leaders with a war crime for deciding to drop the atomic bomb on Hiroshima and Nagasaki.

Unit 5. Postwar to Millennium

Worksheet 1: Cold War Origins (page 80)

1. Establish a global system of naval and air bases, build up its arsenal of arms and develop new weapons, prepare for a future war against the Soviet Union, strive for world domination through imperialism. All accurate, except that the United States was interested in promoting democratic governments rather than establishing actual imperialist colonies, and was not planning on a first-strike war against the Soviet Union, which Novikov seems to imply.

2. General disruption of Western politics, economies, and societies by promoting unrest and dissent; to subvert governments opposed to Soviet interests; to impose nondemocratic, communist-style rule globally; to foment rivalries among Western democracies. All accurate to varying degrees.

3. Each side would see the other as an implacable enemy determined on world conquest and destruction of the rival; adoption of defensive

measures and aggressive countermoves would be seen as essential.

Worksheet 2:
U.S. Cold War Policies (page 81)

Examples will vary; samples are given below.

1. Containment; policy of working to stop, or "contain," the spread of Soviet communist power, control, and influence around the world; Truman Doctrine and the giving of aid to Greece and Turkey to counter Soviet moves

2. Brinkmanship; Dulles policy of declaring that the United States would combat Soviet aggressive moves by going right to the brink of nuclear war, and over the brink, if necessary; Cuban missile crisis

3. Domino theory; idea that if one nation (especially in Asia) "fell" to communism, then others would soon follow—like a row of dominoes that knock each other down, one by one, after the first one goes down; justification for Vietnam War

4. Détente; policy of dealing with the U.S.S.R. in a practical, flexible way; Nixon's visit to the Soviet Union in 1972, the SALT Treaty

Worksheet 3: The Cold War Around the World (page 82)

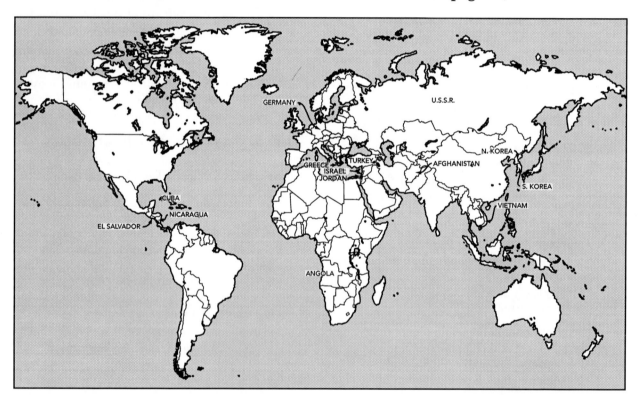

Students could expand this activity to include other Cold War conflict areas and instances.

1. Cuba: 1962, Cuban missile crisis; United States demands removal of Soviet missiles from Cuba.

2. Nicaragua: 1981–90; U.S. backs anticommunist rebels, U.S.S.R. backs communist Sandinista rulers.

3. El Salvador: 1979–92; U.S. backs government against Soviet-backed socialist rebels.

4. Greece: 1946–49; U.S. helps defeat communist-led rebels.

5. Turkey: 1947–50; U.S. gives economic and military aid to rebuff Soviet advances.

6. Germany: 1948; Western democracies airlift supplies to Berlin, blockaded by the U.S.S.R.

7. Israel/Arab neighbors: 1960s to present; U.S. aid supports Israel, Soviet aid supports Arabs.

8. Vietnam: 1947–75; war between north and south; China and U.S.S.R. back native communists; U.S. backs noncommunists in south.

9. Korea: 1950–53; war between communist north and noncommunist south, with backing by U.S.S.R. and China (north) and U.S./U.N. (south).

10. Afghanistan: 1979–89; U.S. arms rebels who fight Soviet occupation.

11. U.S.S.R.: 1960; Soviets shoot down a U.S. U-2 spy plane over Soviet heartland.

12. Angola: 1975–1990s; U.S. and U.S.S.R. back rival sides in a long civil war.

Worksheet 4: The Arab-Israeli Conflict: Origins (page 83)

To extend students' investigation of the Arab-Israeli conflict, see the mapping and time line suggestion in the Additional Activity Suggestions.

1. They are descendants of the people who lived in the region since the dawn of human history; they are currently a majority of the population and have a right to reject immigration of Jews to their land.

2. The Jewish people originated in Palestine; they left involuntarily, have always wanted to return, and thus have a right to return; the right of the Jews to a homeland in Palestine has been recognized by the Balfour Declaration and the League of Nations.

3. Answers will vary; the most skilled diplomats and mediators have not been able to resolve this issue. You could treat this question as an Extra Challenge activity, with groups of students researching the issue further and developing their own suggested solutions, ones that might have been effective in the late 1940s and ones that might be effective today.

Worksheet 5: Africa: Paths to Nationhood (page 84)

1. South Africa; Zimbabwe/Southern Rhodesia

2. Algeria

3. Namibia

4. Angola; Mozambique

5. Kenya

6. Tanzania

7. Ghana

8. Nigeria

9. Congo/Zaire

10. Uganda

11. Sudan

Worksheet 6: Protest: Nonviolent and Violent (page 85)

Students' responses will vary. After reading the statements, you could discuss with the class the differences among the forms of violence that Mandela mentions—sabotage, guerrilla warfare, terrorism, and open revolution. The sabotage that Mandela and his compatriots planned, according to his defense statements, were "Attacks on the economic life lines of the country . . . linked with sabotage on Government buildings and other symbols of apartheid." Students should consider whether such acts would, as Mandela claimed, not involve loss of life.

Worksheet 7: Postwar Latin America (page 86)

Students can write brief answers on the worksheet, or you can have them provide more complete answers on separate sheets.

1. Zapatistas: Rebels of Mexico's Chiapas state, they have named themselves after revolutionary hero Emiliano Zapata; they have demanded greater democracy and better living conditions for Mexico's poorest people, especially the Mayan Indians. The Zapatistas turned to violence because they felt they had no voice in the one-party government.

2. guerrilla: literally, "little war," a guerrilla is a person who takes part in irregular warfare, such as hit-and-run raids; guerrilla warfare has disrupted life in many Latin American nations in the latter part of the twentieth century (e.g., Mexico, Nicaragua, El Salvador, Guatemala, Peru).

3. coca: plant widely grown in Colombia, Bolivia, and Peru from which cocaine is extracted; drug lords in those countries make great profits and hold much power; the U.S. presses governments of those nations to be active in its "war on drugs" and suppress the cocaine trade.

4. *decamisado:* literally, "shirtless one"; term for the urban poor who were fervent supporters of populist president Juan Perón in Argentina in the 1950s

5. *maquiladora:* assembly plant along Mexico's northern border, with the United States; these plants proliferated in the 1980s. Owned by multinational corporations, the plants use cheap Mexican labor to assemble imported parts, mostly for electronic goods and cars. The finished products are trucked into the States and exported elsewhere. The plants provide (nonunionized) jobs but create pollution.

6. *contrarevolucionarios:* counterrevolutionaries, known for short as contras; secretly backed by U.S. President Ronald Reagan, Contras opposed to the reforming nationalist Sandinistas disrupted life in Nicaragua in the 1970s and 1980s. The U.S. Iran-Contra affair revolved around secret weapons sales to Iran to raise money for secret aid to the Contras.

7. *favela:* sprawling shantytown that surrounds a Latin American city, home to multitudes of desperately poor people who live there without running water, electricity, or sewer systems; glaring evidence of the enormous gap between rich and poor

8. *desaparecidos:* "the disappeared"; the thousands of opponents, mostly young people, of Argentina's brutal military rulers during the 1970s and 1980s; the Argentine army kidnapped, tortured, and murdered thousands of people, many of whom "disappeared" after being seized by the military.

Worksheet 8:
Communist Policy Shifts (page 87)

1. Some small enterprise and joint ventures with foreign interests

2. Noncentral (non-state-run) economy, individual initiative and rights, open discussion and criticism of the state

3. Mostly, state ownership of almost everything; complete dictatorship. Gorbachev allows for open discussion and objections to state policy.

4. China has become an attractive target for foreign investment and foreign trade goods, while human rights and freedoms remain firmly quashed. Gorbachev's policy of openness and attempts at creating a market economy caused the Soviet Union and its empire to collapse.

Worksheet 9:
East and Southeast Asia (page 88)

1. Taiwan: 1949 (as Chinese Nationalist nation); Taipei; PCI $16,500

2. South Korea: 1948; Seoul; PCI $12,600

3. Cambodia: 1954; Phnom Penh; PCI $700

4. Philippines: 1946; Manila; PCI $3,500

5. Japan: always independent; Tokyo; PCI $23,100

6. Hong Kong: (not independent, reverted to China from British in 1997); PCI $25,100

7. North Korea: 1948; Pyongyang; PCI $1,000

8. Laos: 1954; Vientiane; PCI $1,260

9. Myanmar (Burma): 1948; Yangon (Rangoon); PCI $1,200

10. China: always independent; Beijing; PCI $3,600

11. Singapore: 1957 as part of Malaya, 1965 as independent city-state; Singapore; PCI $26,300

12. Vietnam: 1954 (as two nations, North Vietnam and South Vietnam; united 1974); Hanoi; PCI $1,770

13. Thailand: always independent; Bangkok; PCI $6,100

14. Indonesia: 1949; Jakarta; PCI $2,830

15. Malaysia: 1957; Kuala Lumpur; PCI $10,300

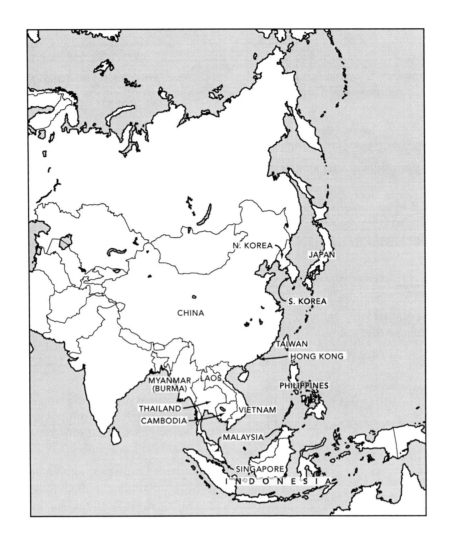

Worksheet 10: Nationalist Leaders of Asia and Africa (page 89)

1. e	5. l	9. k
2. j	6. c	10. f
3. b	7. h	11. g
4. i	8. d	12. a

Additional Activity Suggestions

You could have students do any of the following additional activities.

1. Create maps of the Korean and Vietnam wars, showing major battles and movements, and boundaries before and after each conflict.

2. Research and report on one of the female political leaders of Asian nations in the latter half of the twentieth century, such as Corazón Aquino, Benazir Bhutto, Indira Gandhi, and Golda Meir. Or report on Burmese democratic activist Aung San Suu Kyi.

3. On a map of Eastern Europe and the lands of the former U.S.S.R., show the national changes that resulted from the policies Gorbachev launched.

4. Chart governmental changes in Latin America from the 1930s through the early 2000s. What patterns do you see?

5. Map the changes in Israeli boundaries from 1948 to the present. Create a time line to accompany the map, detailing the events of

the Israeli-Arab struggle and attempts to settle the conflict.

6. Research and report on the conflict between India and Pakistan over Kashmir, beginning with partition of the subcontinent and continuing to the present.

7. Investigate any of these Internet sites:

"Africa Online: Kids' Zone":
http://lagos.africaonline.com/site/africa/kids.jsp

"Chronology of Russian History":
http://www.departments.bucknell.edu/russian/chrono3.html

"Cold War Hot Links":
http://www.stmartin.edu/~dprice/cold.war.html

"Cold War International History Project":
http://cwihp.si.edu/default.htm

"K–12 Electronic Guide for African Resources on the Internet":
http://www.sas.upenn.edu/African_Studies/K-12/menu_EduMEDI.html

"LANIC: Latin American Newtwork Information Center":
http://lanic.utexas.edu/las.html

"Mid East: Going Back to Full-Blown War?":
http://www.megastories.com/mideast/index.shtml

"Quotations from Chairman Mao Tse-tung":
http://art-bin.com/art/omaotoc.html

"Seeds of Peace":
http://www.seedsofpeace.org/

"Vietnam: Yesterday and Today":
http://servercc.oakton.edu/~wittman

Assessment

1. Have students create annotated time lines of independence movements and achievements in Asia and Africa during the twentieth century.

2. Have students trace current world tensions and conflicts to Cold War origins.

Unit 6. The Modern Global World

Worksheet 1:
Science and Technology (page 95)

Students' answers will vary somewhat. Here are samples.

1. Computer use: benefits—information revolution, creates global information and communication network; disadvantages—overuse results in loss of physical fitness, isolation of individuals, lack of personal contact.

2. Genetic engineering: benefits—leads to important therapies to treat disease, improved plant strains; disadvantages—privacy concerns, crossbreeding of genetically altered plants with nongenetically altered plants with yet unknown consequences

3. Cloning: benefits—possible treatments for currently untreatable diseases and conditions; disadvantages—ethical issues about creating and altering life

4. Technology replacing human workers: benefits—speeds up production, avoids human error, cuts costs; disadvantages—fewer jobs available for people

5. Green Revolution: benefits—new strains of crop plants yield much more food per acre to feed growing populations and avoid famine; disadvantages—new strains require chemical fertilizers and pesticides, harvesting machinery, and in some cases irrigation systems, so only well-off farmers and agribusinesses benefit, while poor peasants are forced off the land.

Worksheet 2:
Adventures in Space (page 96)

1. Sun: 1969, *Pioneer 9*

2. Earth: October 1957, *Sputnik*

3. Earth's moon: (unmanned) September 1959, *Luna 2;* (manned) July 1969, *Apollo 11*

4. Saturn: November 1980, *Voyager 1*

5. Neptune: August 1989, *Voyager 1*

6. Venus: May 1969, *Venera 5*

7. Mercury: March 1974, *Mariner 10*

8. Mars: July 1976, *Viking 1*

9. Jupiter: March 1979, *Voyager 1*

10. Uranus: January 1986, *Voyager 2*

Worksheet 3: U.N. Peacekeeping (page 97)

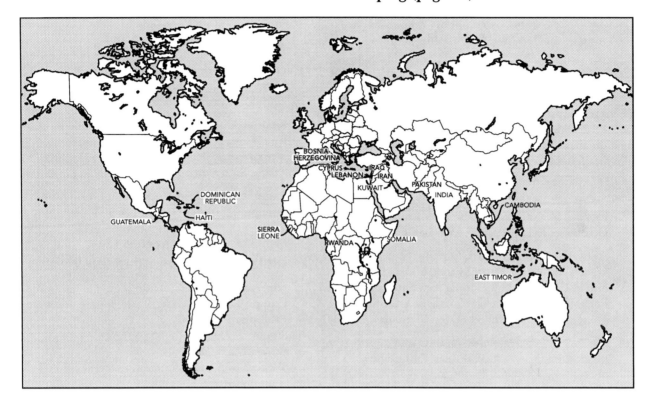

Students should show each country on their map of the world.

1. India-Pakistan: 1949; U.N. arranges a cease-fire in the disputed territory of Kashmir.

2. East Timor: 1999; U.N. oversees a referendum on East Timorese independence from Indonesia after much violence.

3. Rwanda: 1993; U.N. intervenes in vicious Tutsi-Hutu civil war.

4. Iraq/Kuwait: 1991; U.S.-led U.N. forces oust invading Iraqi troops from Kuwait; U.N. imposes sanctions on Iraq.

5. Iran/Iraq: 1988; U.N. helps implement a cease-fire to the lengthy war between these two nations.

6. Cyprus: 1964; U.N. steps in to maintain peace between rival Greek and Turkish populations.

7. Dominican Republic: 1965; U.N. peacekeeping force oversees cease-fire between leftist rebels and successors to long-time dictator Trujillo.

8. Cambodia: 1991; U.N. brokers withdrawal of Vietnamese forces, who had invaded to oust Pol Pot and his Khmer Rouge.

9. Sierra Leone: 1998; backed by Nigerian-led coalition of troops, U.N. intervenes in civil war between elected civilian government and military rebels.

10. Somalia: 1992; U.N. directs relief efforts during severe famine and civil war.

11. Lebanon: 1958; U.N. tries to restore peace in Lebanon's civil war among Christians and Muslims.

12. Bosnia and Herzegovina: 1995; U.N. tries to maintain peace agreement among Bosnia's Muslims, Croats, and Serbs.

13. Guatemala: 1997; U.N. helps enforce peace agreement that ended Latin America's longest-running civil war, between right-wing military governments and leftist rebels.

14. Haiti: 1994; U.N. peacekeeping force, led by the United States, ousts military rulers and restores elected president to office.

Worksheet 4: World Trade Blocs (page 98)

You could divide the class into small groups, with each one identifying member nations from two or three of the named trade blocs. Each would then show the areas that their blocs encompass on a world map which, when completed, would show the plethora of regional trading blocs that exist around the world.

1. Andean Community of Nations—Bolivia, Colombia, Ecuador, Peru, Venezuela

2. APEC—Australia, Brunei, Canada, Chile, China, Indonesia, Japan, Korea, Malaysia, Mexico, New Zealand, Papua New Guinea, Peru, Philippines, Russia, Singapore, Chinese Taipei, Thailand, United States, Vietnam

3. ASEAN—Brunei, Cambodia, Darussalam, Indonesia, Laos, Malaysia, Myanmar, Philippines, Singapore, Thailand, Vietnam

4. CARICOM—Antigua and Barbuda, Bahamas, Barbados, Belize, Dominica, Grenada, Guyana, Haiti, Jamaica, Montserrat, St. Kitts and Nevis, St. Lucia, Surinam, St. Vincent and the Grenadines, Trinidad and Tobago

5. COMESA—Angola, Burundi, Comoros, Democratic Republic of Congo, Djibouti, Egypt, Eritrea, Ethiopia, Kenya, Madagascar, Malawi, Mauritius, Namibia, Rwanda, Seychelles, Sudan, Swaziland, Uganda, Zambia, Zimbabwe

6. CIS—Armenia, Azerbaijan, Belarus, Georgia, Kazakhstan, Kyrgystan, Moldova, Russia, Tajikistan, Turkmenistan, Ukraine, Uzbekistan

7. Council of Arab Economic Unity—Egypt, Iraq, Jordan, Kuwait, Libya, Mauritania, Palestine Liberation Organization, Somalia, Sudan, Syria, United Arab Emirates, Yemen

8. ECOWAS—Benin, Burkina Faso, Cabo Verde, Cote d'Ivoire, Gambia, Ghana, Guinée, Guinée Bissau, Liberia, Mali, Niger, Nigeria, Senegal, Sierra Leone, Togolese Republic

9. EU—Belgium, Denmark, Germany, Greece, Spain, France, Ireland, Italy, Luxembourg, Netherlands, Austria, Portugal, Finland, Sweden, United Kingdom

10. NAFTA—Canada, Mexico, United States

11. OPEC—Algeria, Indonesia, Iran, Iraq, Kuwait, Libya, Nigeria, Qatar, Saudi Arabia, United Arab Emirates, Venezuela

12. SADC—Angola, Botswana, Democratic Republic of Congo, Lesotho, Malawi, Mauritius, Mozambique, Namibia, Seychelles, South Africa, Swaziland, Tanzania, Zambia, Zimbabwe

13. Southern Common Market—Argentina, Brazil, Paraguay, Uruguay

Worksheet 5: World Population Growth (pages 99–100)

1. Nigeria: 3,265,600
   Congo: 1,444,400
   Ethiopia: 1,287,400
   Sudan: 942,000
   Egypt: 1,228,300
   Turkey: 1,036,600
   Iraq: 830,700
   China: 10,638,600
   India: 16,539,000
   Brazil: 2,090,400
   Mexico: 1,739,400
   United States: 2,366,400

2. 96%

3. Region, most: Asia and Oceania

   Region, least: More Developed Countries

   Country, most: India

4. India's total population will outstrip China's if this trend continues.

5. A population explosion took place between 1927 and 1974; from 1974 to 1999, the rate of population growth declined somewhat; projections indicate a renewed increase in the rate of population growth, especially between 2026 and 2043.

Worksheet 6: Urban Growth (page 101)

1. 1950—30%; 1975—37%; 2000—50%; 2025—60%

2. The percentage of people living in urban areas increases by about 10 percent every 25 years.

3. Students' answers will vary somewhat. Here are suggestions.

   Social: Nuclear family replaces extended family of the village; urban values (e.g., materialism, job status) undermine traditional rural values; culture shock sets in; but education is more available, and leisure-time attractions are many.

   Economic: Jobs offer escape from rural poverty, but many arrivals from the countryside cannot find jobs and live in appalling conditions in urban shantytowns.

   Environmental: Cities become ringed by shanty-towns; sewerage and garbage pollute the area, as well as industrial by-products.

Worksheet 7: The World's Environment (page 102)

1. Pollution (water, air)

   Causes: Emissions from factories, cars, trucks, energy-producing plants; leaching and runoff of pesticides and chemical fertilizer into groundwater, ponds, lakes, streams; storm water discharge; release of chlorofluorocarbons (CFCs)

   Effects: Contaminated drinking water; smog; respiratory problems; acid rain; aquatic life die-off; thinning of ozone layer

2. Species extinction

   Causes: Habitat destruction; pollution; overhunting

   Effects: Reduction of global biodiversity; ecosystem imbalance; loss of food and medical resources

3. Deforestation

   Causes: Taking of forests for farms, living areas, roads, and wood products

   Effects: Erosion; loss of wildlife habitat; species extinction (animal and plant); climate alterations due to loss of carbon-dioxide-absorbing trees

4. Erosion, desertification

   Causes: Overgrazing, overfarming and poor farming techniques, and climate changes

   Effects: Loss of arable land, reduced food production

5. Garbage accumulation

   Causes: Growing population, growing urban areas, growing industry, wasteful packaging

   Effects: Pollution and associated health hazards; land devoted to garbage dumps and landfills rather than to productive uses

Worksheet 8: The Earth's Future: Two Views (page 103)

Students' responses will vary.

Worksheet 9: Viewpoints: The Muslim Middle East, the United States, and Terrorism (page 104)

Student responses will vary; emphasize that the students should evaluate from an impartial—non-Muslim, non-U.S.—point of view, to the best of their ability. You could break the class into small groups, with each one evaluating several of the expressions. Or you could assign one group of students to the impartial panel, another group to explain one or more of these perceptions more thoroughly, and a third group to respond from the U.S. point of view.

Additional Activity Suggestions

You could have students do any of the following additional tasks.

1. Prepare for a class discussion/debate about the issues of global responsibility to protect the environment. What responsibility do the indus-trialized nations have to reduce environmental damage? How should developing nations balance economic needs and environmental responsibility? How can environmental protec-tion be paid for, and by whom?

2. Draw up a time line of weapons control agree-ments since the 1950s.

3. Create a chart of ethnic and religious conflicts around the world from the 1970s to the present.

4. Find statistics on world population migrations in the later years of the twentieth century, and present your findings on a world map, supported by a graph or chart of statistics.

5. Research and report on the programs and impacts of one of the United Nations' social service agencies.

6. Research and report on the uses of the many satellites currently orbiting our planet. Or, create a class display of images sent back by spacecraft of aspects of our solar system and beyond.

7. Investigate how various countries have fought terrorism/terrorist groups within their borders, such as West Germany (the Red Army Faction), Italy (the Red Brigades), Northern Ireland (Protestant and Catholic extremists), Israel (various terror groups such as HAMAS), Egypt (militant Islamic terrorists), and Japan (the sarin nerve gas attack).

8. With classmates, construct a time line of major terrorist events from the late 1960s to the present. You could create a series of parallel time lines sorted by general tactic, such as kidnapping, plane hijacking, plane bombing, truck and car bombing, ship attack, individual suicide bombers, assassination, cross-border raids, and biochemical attacks. Include dates, place, responsible party, and nature of the event.

9. Investigate any of these Internet sites:

"Constitutional Rights Foundation: America Responds to Terrorism":
http://www.crf-usa.org/terror/America%20Responds%20to%20Terrorism.htm

"The Environment: A Global Challenge":
http://library.thinkquest.org/26026/

"Global Poverty":
http://www.mtholyoke.edu/acad/intrel/poverty.htm

"International Human Rights Instruments":
http://www1.umn.edu/humanrts/instree/ainstls1.htm

"John W. Mauchly and the Development of the ENIAC Computer":
http://www.library.upenn.edu/special/gallery/mauchly/jwmintro.html

"Multinational Corporations":
http://www.mtholyoke.edu/acad/intrel/mnc.htm

"NASA Human Spaceflight":
http://spaceflight.nasa.gov/

"PBS: Looking for Answers" (9/11 terrorist attacks):
http://www.pbs.org/wgbh/pages/frontline/shows/terrorism/

"PBS: Target America":
http://www.pbs.org/wgbh/pages/frontline/shows/target/

"United Nations Peacekeeping":
http://www.un.org/Depts/dpko/dpko/home.shtml

"World Popclock":
http://www.census.gov/cgi-bin/ipc/popclockw

"World Trade Organization":
http://www.wto.org/

"The World Wide Web History Project":
http://www.webhistory.org/home.html

Assessment

1. Have students create a chart or graph that demonstrates the global widening of the gap between rich and poor.

2. Ask interested students to assess the extent of the "McDonaldization" of the world and to develop an argument for or against the global spread of the elements of Western culture and economics.

ADDITIONAL RESOURCES

Literature

Chinua Achebe, *Things Fall Apart*

Pearl Buck, *The Good Earth*

T. S. Eliot, *The Waste Land*

Anne Frank, *The Diary of a Young Girl*

Ernest Hemingway, *For Whom the Bell Tolls* and *The Sun Also Rises*

Ba Jin, *Family*

Naguib Mahfouz, *Midaq Alley*

Kamala Markandaya, *Nectar in a Sieve*

George Orwell, *Animal Farm* and *1984*

Boris Pasternak, *Doctor Zhivago*

Erich Maria Remarque, *All Quiet on the Western Front*

Mikhail Sholokhov, *And Quiet Flows the Don*

Khushwant Singh, *Train to Pakistan*

Alexander Solzhenitsyn, *August 1914* and *One Day in the Life of Ivan Denisovich*

War poetry of Rupert Brooke, Wilfred Owen, and Siegfried Sassoon

Elie Wiesel, *Night*

Collections of Primary Source Documents: Print

Andrea, Alfred J., and James H. Overfield. *The Human Record: Sources of Global History* (Vol. 2). Boston: Houghton Mifflin, 2001.

Frazee, Charles, ed. *World History: Original and Secondary Source Readings* (Vol. 2). San Diego: Greenhaven Press, 1999.

Hughes, Sarah Shaver and Brady. *Women in World History* (Vol. 2). Armonk, NY: M.E. Sharpe, 1997.

Kishlansky, Mark A., ed. *Sources of World History: Readings for World Civilization* (Vol. 2). New York: HarperCollins, 1995.

Reilly, Kevin, ed. *Worlds of History: A Comparative Reader* (Vol. 2). Boston: Bedford/St. Martins Press, 2000.

Riley, Philip F., et al. *The Global Experience: Readings in World History* (Vol. 2). Englewood Cliffs, NJ: Prentice Hall, 1998.

Stearns, Peter, ed. *World History in Documents: A Comparative Reader.* New York: New York University Press, 1998.

Weisner, Merry E., et al., eds. *Discovering the Global Past: A Look at the Evidence* (Vol. 2), 2d ed. Boston: Houghton Mifflin, 2002.

CD-ROM

Carmen Sandiego's Great Chase Through Time (Broderbund)

Chronicle Encyclopedia of History (Dorling Kindersley)

The Complete National Geographic (Mindscape)

Encarta Africana and *Encarta Interactive World* (Microsoft)

Geosafari History (Educational Insights)

Historical Images on CD-ROM: World History (Instructional Resources Corp.)

History and Culture of Africa (Queue)

Lest We Forget: A History of the Holocaust (Logos Research Systems)

Material World (Starpress)

National Geographic Maps (Mindscape)

The Story of Civilization by Will and Ariel Durant (World Library)

Timeliner (Tom Snyder)

Time Traveler CD: A Multimedia Chronicle of History (New Media Schoolhouse)

20th Century Day by Day (Dorling Kindersley)

World Discovery Plus (Great Wave)

World History: ResourceLink—20th Century (ABC-CLIO)

World History Series (*Imperialism; Causes of World War I; The Russian Revolution; Fascist Dictatorships; Causes of World War II; Twentieth Century Nationalism;* also available on video) (Clearvue)

Video/DVD

A&E Biography Series (numerous titles, covering world leaders, entrepreneurs, scientists and inventors, Anne Frank) (A&E)

Africa: A Voyage of Discovery with Basil Davidson Series (RM Arts)

African Art and Culture (Clearvue)

China in the 20th Century (Landmark Media)

Doctor Strangelove or: How I Learned to Stop Worrying and Love the Bomb (Columbia)

Gandhi (Columbia)

The Great Dictator (Charlie Chaplin on Hitler) (20th Century Fox Home Entertainment)

History Through Art: The Twentieth Century (Clearvue)

History's Turning Points Series (*The Russian Revolution, The Atom Bomb, The Battle of Britain, The Incredible March, Crisis in Korea, The Battle for Vietnam*) (Ambrose)

Invention (3 vols.) (Discovery Communications)

South America Series (Encyclopedia Britannica)

Tora! Tora! Tora! (20th Century-Fox)

The 20th Century (MPI)

Understanding World War I (Educational Video Network)

Witness: Voices from the Holocaust (Stories To Remember)

The World: A Television History (*The End of the Old Order: 1900–1929; The World in Conflict: 1929–1945; The Modern World: 1945–1980*) (Network Television Production)

World Wide Web/Internet

Sites with numerous links to world history sources are listed below. Sites of more specific interest are listed where appropriate in the Answers and Additional Activities section. Be aware that URLs do change, and sites vanish. If a URL listed here yields no results, try searching with the site title given below.

"The Avalon Project at the Yale Law School" (a large collection of historical documents):
http://www.yale.edu/lawweb/avalon/avalon.htm

"History/Social Studies for K–12 Teachers" (includes site map, What's New Archive, sources arranged by category):
http://my.execpc.com/~dboals/boals.html

"WWW-VL History Central Catalog" (University of Kansas site with links to every imaginable aspect of history):
http://www.ukans.edu/history/VL/

"Internet History Sourcebooks Project" (amazing site for primary sources in many specific areas of history/geography):
http://www.fordham.edu/halsall/

"Kathy Schrock's Guide for Educators—World and Ancient History Sites" (a Cape Cod teacher's excellent list of resources):
http://school.discovery.com/schrockguide/history/histw.html

GLOSSARY

alliance—agreement among two or more nations that each will come to the aid of one of the others if it is attacked by any other country

appeasement—policy of giving in to the demands of an aggressor

armistice—agreement to end fighting; a truce

assassination—murder by sudden attack for political or ideological reasons

assembly line—manufacturing system using conveyer belts and standardized parts to speed assembly

autocracy—government under a ruler who has absolute power

blitzkrieg—"lightning war," swift action taken against another nation

bloc—combination of groups or nations united by a common interest or purpose

caste—Hindu social class that a person is born into

civil disobedience—deliberate, public refusal to obey a law perceived as unjust

coalition—temporary alliance of several political parties

Cold War—the decades-long conflict between the United States and the Soviet Union

collective—large farm controlled by the state and operated by workers as a group

colony—a land controlled by a far-away nation

conservativism—support of the way things are and of only gradual rather than sudden or radical change; a person who adheres to this policy is a **conservative**

coup—sudden overthrow of a government by a small group that seizes power

depression—extended period of low economic activity and high unemployment

developed nations—nations that are industrialized

developing nations—nations that are not much industrialized

dictator—absolute ruler

entente—friendly understanding between nations, as opposed to a formal alliance

fascism—system led by a dictator that promotes state control of the economy, aggressive nationalism, and suppression of individual rights; a person who supports such a system is a **fascist**

free trade—open trade among nations with no economic barriers

fundamentalist—one who adheres to traditional religious beliefs

genocide—planned killing of most of a racial, political, or cultural group

glasnost—changed Soviet policy of openness

guerrilla—member of a loosely organized fighting force that engages in irregular warfare, such as hit-and-run raids

imperialism—policy of seeking to gain control over other countries

industrial—characterized by highly developed systems for producing goods

inflation—a large and continuing rise in the general level of prices

Internet—global network of linked computers

isolationism—foreign policy of avoiding involvement with other nations

junta—military group that overthrows an elected government

kaiser—a German emperor

mandate—territory run by a Western power after World War I

Marxist—follower of the ideas of Karl Marx, who predicted class warfare between workers and employers

militarism—glorification of the military and a focus on being ready for war

mobilization—a call to active duty of all soldiers of a nation's army

nationalism—deep pride in and devotion to one's country

neutral—condition of not being aligned with either opposing side in a war

New Deal—wide-ranging U.S. government-run program of social and economic reforms adopted in response to the Great Depression

passive resistance—nonviolent refusal to obey laws perceived as unjust

peasant—person of low social rank, usually an agricultural laborer

perestroika—more free restructuring of Soviet economy and government

police state—country in which the police, especially a secret police force, suppress any actions by individuals or groups that conflict with government policy

premier—prime minister, official head of a parliamentary government

progressivism—support of progress, change, improvement, and reform; a person who adheres to this policy is a **progressive**

proletarian—having to do with the working class

propaganda—spreading of ideas or information to help promote a cause

purge—removal of undesirable members of an organization

recession—a slowing down of economic activity

reparations—payments for damages

rural—referring to the country and country life

satellite—nation that is dominated or controlled by another more powerful nation

segregation—legal separation of people by race

socialism—system in which the people as a whole own the means of production—property and businesses; a person who believes in such a system is a **socialist**

soviets—councils of workers and soldiers that formed during the Russian Revolution; the term was then used for the nation's new name, the Union of **Soviet** Socialist Republics, or **Soviet** Union

sphere of influence—area in one nation where trade and investment are controlled by an outside nation

tariff—set of taxes on goods brought into one country from another country

technology—tools and inventions that people develop and use to meet their needs

tenement—apartment building, especially one for lower-class residents

terrorism—use of random acts of violence against civilians to make political points, take revenge, and affect government policies

totalitarianism—government system of total control over all aspects of public and private life

treaty—formal agreement among nations

tsar—Russian imperial ruler

union—an organization of workers

urban—having to do with cities and city life

Zionist—supporter of the movement to establish a Jewish homeland in Palestine

Share Your Bright Ideas with Us!

We want to hear from you! Your valuable comments and suggestions will help us meet your current and future classroom needs.

Your name_____Date_____

School name_____

School address_____

City _____State _____Zip_____Phone number (_____)_____

Grade level taught_____Subject area(s) taught_____Average class size_____

Where did you purchase this publication?_____

Was your salesperson knowledgeable about this product?   Yes_____   No_____

What monies were used to purchase this product?

_____School supplemental budget   _____Federal/state funding   _____Personal

Please "grade" this Walch publication according to the following criteria:

Quality of service you received when purchasing ....A   B   C   D   F

Ease of use...A   B   C   D   F

Quality of content..A   B   C   D   F

Page layout ....A   B   C   D   F

Organization of material ....A   B   C   D   F

Suitability for grade level ....A   B   C   D   F

Instructional value ....A   B   C   D   F

COMMENTS:_____

_____

What specific supplemental materials would help you meet your current—or future—instructional needs?

_____

Have you used other Walch publications? If so, which ones?_____

May we use your comments in upcoming communications?   ___Yes   ___No

Please **FAX** this completed form to **207-772-3105**, or mail it to:

Product Development, J. Weston Walch, Publisher, P. O. Box 658, Portland, ME 04104-0658

We will send you a **FREE GIFT** as our way of thanking you for your feedback. **THANK YOU!**